MR. DOOLEY

ON THE

CHOICE OF LAW

Compiled and Arranged by

EDWARD J. BANDER

THE MICHIE COMPANY

Law Publishers

Charlottesville, Virginia

TO THE KENNEDY ADMINISTRATION

MAY IT HAVE MORE DOOLEYS
THAN HENNESSYS

PREFACE

Mr. Dooley's recall has long been demanded. Such critics as Henry Seidel Canby, Gilbert Seldes and British Denis Brogan . . . such humorists as E. B. White and Stephen Leacock . . . such historians as Mark Sullivan and Foster Rhea Dulles . . . all found his thinking indispensable to their particular fields; but it is the legal profession that owes the greatest debt to Mr. Dooley.

A roster of his legal admirers would list Chief Justice Hughes and Justice Holmes; Justice Frankfurter, who called him "that great philosopher," and cited him in the United States Supreme Court case of A. F. L. v. American Sash Door 335 U. S. 538, 557 (1949); Professors Corwin and Pound who cite him to advantage in their writings—and, we are told, in their classes; Fred Rodell, Bernard Schwartz, and John P. Frank whose recent books on the Supreme Court show a respect for Mr. Dooley's views which may be the only unanimity one can expect from commentators on the Court. The pages of the American Bar Association Journal, official organ of the largest association of lawyers, writes of Mr. Dooley: "Time has come for Law Schools to require that applicants have a knowledge of Finley Peter Dunne and Mr. Dooley. The ones that think like Dooley are sure bets." Arthur J. Keeffe in 44 American Bar Association Journal 996 (1958).

To the uninitiated, Mr. Martin Dooley was the alter ego of Finley Peter Dunne, a journalist whose fame at the turn of the century made him a public idol and the confidante of President Theodore Roosevelt. The Mr. Dooley essays were predicated on current events but like all great literature they achieved immortality by transcending the immediate. Of the approximately five hundred essays that appeared from 1892 to 1914 in Sunday newspapers and magazines throughout the country (about a third of which were reprinted in book form), thirty-nine, some in excerpt, have been selected for the basis of this anthology. These thirty-nine, a good many appearing here in book form for the first time, represent in my opinion the best and most enduring Dooley views on law and politics. Fine as they are, humorous as they are, I regretfully concede that they would not remain nearly as much so if there had been any marked improvement in certain areas of law and order and the attitudes of the gullible public since Mr. Dunne's day, though we could easily go further back than that. As Mr. Dooley said, a smart man can be "buncoed" but not an honest one—a lesson not easily learned.

This collection runs the gamut of the legal profession. The section on trial practice covers the woes of a beleaguered litigant, cross-examination, insanity as a defense and includes one of Dunne's pieces on the Dreyfus case, which he personally covered. Mr. Ellis, in his biography of Finley Peter Dunne, tells us his essay "On Criminals" was read in a certain parish church once every year, and it is a tale that can bring a tear to the eyes of even a hanging judge. "The Art of Advocacy" is a combination of

two essays which, for some unknown reason, I have
never found combined, though each contains part of
the other. I have taken the liberty of making one essay from them. Its portrayal of the law "yesterday
and today" rings even truer now then when it was
written.

The law's delays (now euphemistically termed
'congestion in the courts'), a shibboleth with which
Mr. Dooley makes much, are often referred to—par-
ticularly in the essay "On Criminal Trials" and also in "Freedom of the Press," a too long neglected
essay discovered in an old, now defunct magazine.
"The Big Fine" grew out of the $29,240,000 fine of
John D. Rockefeller by Judge Kenesaw M. Landis,
who became the "czar" of baseball after the White
Sox scandal. As Mr. Dooley suspected would happen, the fine was not paid and if you are interested
in the Court's reasoning see U. S. v. Standard Oil
155 Federal Reporter 305 (1907), reversed in 164
Federal Reporter 376 (1908).

"The Supreme Court's Decision" is the most famous of the Dooley essays relating to the legal profession, but its complete parody of an upper court
opinion has been frequently overlooked in favor of
its much quoted one-liner that the Supreme Court
follows the election returns. The case involved,
Downes v. Bidwell 182 U. S. 244 (1901), must be
read for full appreciation of a less than grand style
of legal writing, aptly termed by John P. Frank in
his "Marble Palace" as "legal massive." Those who
are familiar with James M. Marsh's use of the

Dooley method in his satire "Mr. Dooley discovers a Unanimous Dissent," 62 Case & Comment No. 6, 8 (1957), can see it is still an effective approach. It is interesting to note that Downes v. Bidwell was one of a series of cases popularly known as the "insular Cases" among which was one called Dooley v. U. S., which may well have inspired the entire piece as there is intrinsic evidence in the satire that Dunne had read it.

Associate Justice Brewer's address, given at the Yale Bicentennial in 1901 and here parodied in "College and Degrees," confirms what Justice Holmes subsequently wrote of Brewer: "a very pleasant man in private, but he had the itch for public speaking and writing and made me shudder many times." 1 Holmes-Pollock Letters 160, April 1, 1910.

Mr. Dooley's views on marriage and divorce and the rights of women, including the right to vote, are not those currently held; although I suspect there are those of both sexes who still believe he was right. It may be only incidental that Finley Peter Dunne's output diminished rapidly after the Nineteenth Amendment. He once said, in commenting upon female athletes, that he would never marry a woman he could not lick in a fight, and one can only assume that this included combat of a political nature. Mr. Dooley in these essays on the rights of women expresses a sentiment once held by law that man and woman are one and man is the one.

Probably Dunne's hardest hitting essay (rivalled only by his suggestion to union hating coal magnate

Baer that if, as he himself had suggested, God was
his partner, then an accounting was due—on Mr.
Baer see the essay in this volume on "Property
Rights") concerned President Theodore Roosevelt's
luncheon with Booker T. Washington. Mr. Dooley
did not see issues in black and white; he cut through
to the essence of the problem and should leave the
majority of his readers feeling not righteous, but
wondering if there is anyone qualified to throw the
first stone. Professor Filler in his introduction to
"Mr. Dooley Now and Forever" has most ably inter-
preted the Dunne approach to the problem of prejudice. Legal philosopher Paul Sayre wrote in his
biography of Dean Pound, "Hatred of hypocrisy in
every form is perhaps the vital force in all of Mr.
Dooley's criticisms of men and matters. It is the
moral equilibrium that enables Dooley to deal with
varied subjects fairly, with complete dignity from
his point of view, and with the cheerful freshness of
all his thoughts."

As indicated earlier, both the humor and the
tragedy of Dooley's pieces is that they still have so
much bearing on our own times. On labor relations,
immigration and the other items in the Administra-
tive Law section of this book, one will find that the
law has changed little and those who make the law,
the people, even less. We have the same problem of
the poor man having the same chance in a court of
law as he has outside it, as Mr. Dooley said; and it
is hoped that a rereading or a first reading by a new
generation may bring fresh perspective to bear on

some old problems, and may even suggest some solutions to our statesmen.

It was not my original intention to include what seemed to me Mr. Dooley's rather skeptical views on international relations in this collection. Finley Peter Dunne was a Midwesterner, and an Irishman whose suspicion of the English may have unduly influenced his views (he once had Mr. Dooley say "whin England purrishes th' Irish'll die iv what Hogan calls ongwee, which is havin' no wan in th' weary wurruld ye don't love"). Yet the cynicism with which he eyed the possibility of international cooperation was to prove sadly more realistic than the mist of utopian pipe dreams of the pre-World War I era. And while it may not follow from Mr. Dooley's suggestion that because a law suit leaves more "hard feelin's" than a good fight the latter method is the better course to pursue, still, it is a view that our experts on international relations must take to the bargaining table with them. Be that as it may, my task in bringing the jurisprudential essays of Mr. Dooley together would not be complete without a sampling of his international law selections.

Whether law is a branch of politics I cannot say, except that no law school offers a course in this field to which so many lawyers are attracted. To make up for this seeming lack, I recommend the Mr. Dooley essays included herein to those who plan a career in politics after law school. One of Mr. Dooley's revelations is that a politician never knows he

is bribed the first time—the second time he asks for
it. He was not as much concerned with who did the
voting as he was with who did the counting. There
are many other black letter rules. President Theodore Roosevelt's libel trial, which includes a discussion of drink and statesmanship, and Dooley's views
on the once popular recall and referendum add a
course in history and biography, essential elements
for the compleat politician.

"On Making a Will" has been included in the section of this volume which also includes by virtue of
the pure enjoyment to be had in the reading, essays
on golf and yacht clubs, though if one reads these
pieces closely and notices the frequent use of legal
terms, he might agree with me that four hundred
years from now Dunne's authorship may be challenged and a lawyer—Adlai Stevenson, for example,
"proven" to be the real author.

The last section consists of imitations of Mr.
Dooley for which the compiler assumes most of the
responsibility. No one can have lived six years with
Mr. Dooley and not, on occasion, feel the urge to respond to the problems of the day as he felt Mr.
Dooley would. That one should include the imitation next to the original is an act of heroism that
gives credence to Mr. Dooley's view that all heroes
are half fools.

Believing that acknowledgments are too often in-
direct expressions of self-importance, insecurity and
saccharine insincerity, I am going to single out only
three people to whom I feel prime indebtedness . . .

Finley Peter Dunne, whose work has not only made mine possible, but my life a more rewarding experience . . . Preston Slack, mailman extraordinary, for reading Mr. Dooley essays to me in his fine Irish brogue when I was Librarian of the United States Court of Appeals in Boston . . . and myself.

Compilers are an all too neglected breed and only one who has spent years of similar searching and seizing can appreciate the joys and pangs of following every thread of evidence to locate every Mr. Dooley item. Extended correspondence, endless searching of indexes (one must learn to check not only under Dunne but also Dunn, Mr. Dooley and Dooley), the writing of articles, putting up of exhibits (at the law libraries of New York University, Harvard University, Yale University and the Bar Association of the City of New York at this writing) are but part of the time consuming efforts contributed to the cause of being a devoted servant to another man's genius.

EDWARD J. BANDER

TABLE OF CONTENTS

MR. DOOLEY AT COURT

1. Trial Practice—Civil and Uncivil

2. Appellate Practice—Some Rebuttable Presumptions of Mr. Dooley

3. Constitutional Law—Mr. Dooley Speaks for the Supreme Court

MR. DOOLEY ON ADMINISTRATIVE LAW

MR. DOOLEY ON INTERNATIONAL LAW

POLITICS—A BRANCH OF THE LAW

RELAXATION—A YACHT CLUB, SAYS MR. DOOLEY, IS AN ASSOCIATION OF LAWYERS

MR. DOOLEY IMITATED—"A GOOD MANNY PEOPLE R-READ TH' OL' SAYIN': 'LARCENY IS TH' SINCEREST FORM IV FLATTERY.'"

INTRODUCTION

Mark Twain was wont to call himself a philosopher. Finley Dunne had the same power of seeing the universal side of a passing humorous situation or occurrence and putting it in epigrammatic form. Martin Dooley, the philosopher of "Archey Road, beyant the thracks and forninst the gas house," looked at the humorous aspects of the events of the time sub specie aeternitatis. [A recent philosopher wrote a book on the philosophy of "As If."] Mark Twain tells how after Tom Sawyer, who knew from his reading of books of adventures that the established mode of digging a captive out of prison was to use a case knife, went to work diligently to dig Jim out of the cabin where he was confined. But after he and Huck Finn had dug for hours and their hands were blistered and they had made little progress, a light came to Tom. He dropped his knife and said to Huck, "Gimme a case knife." Huck saw the point and gave him a pickaxe, and Tom went to work with it. That was just like Tom, said Huck: "Full of principle." In like fashion when every one was speaking of the Anglo-Saxon Alliance, Mr. Dooley explained: "Hinnessy, I'm an Anglo-Saxon and you're an Anglo-Saxon, and Tiddy Rosenfelt he's an Anglo-Saxon." In the era of Anti-slavery agitation and the prelude to the Civil War, James Russell Lowell spoke through Hosey Biglow and the pedant schoolmaster Homer Wilbur. In the era of entrance of the United States into World Politics,

Martin Dooley and Hinnessy spoke from Dooley's place on Archey Road.

He was a good-humored but incisive critic of catch phrases and fashions of thought of the moment. When orators were declaiming about how Leonidas held the pass at Thermopylae it reminded Mr. Dooley of how Casey "held the polin' place of the fighting precinct of the first ward." When every one was reciting the exploits of Garcia, the addressee of President McKinley's famous letter, Mr. Dooley explained how the rebel Garcia took to the brush with forty rounds of canned lobster. When there was general discussion of "the crime of '73" and the need of stable currency, Mr. Dooley explained that if people wanted something "that niver fluctocates, which is odd considering how much of it goes down, something that was fifteen cents a slug and two for a quarther before the crime of 'siventy three and fifteen cints a slug and two for a quarther after the crime of 'seventy three they should relocate the mint at the distillery and lave it stay there." When the papers were full of discussions of the constitutionality of acquisition of territory by the federal government and whether the constitution followed the flag, Mr. Dooley explained that at any rate the Supreme Court "follows the illiction rethurns." When, at the close of the Spanish American War Chauncey M. Depew and others sent congratulatory messages to President McKinley, Mr. Dooley joined with the message: "Mack, ye done noble, Dooley."

When in the war between Greece and Bulgaria the Greeks were badly defeated from the start, Mr. Dooley explained that because of raising of rent and "throuble with the landlord" it could not be assumed that "the same tinent always lived in the wan house. The Miltiadeses and Leonidases and Caseys and O'Houlihans muves on and their place is tuk be Swades an' Bohamians."

Often it was hard to make out the detailed facts of much discussed and controverted happenings. When Zola wrote his famous challenge of the Dreyfus investigation, Dooley explained how Zola thumbed his nose at the court and said "Jackuse, which is the divil of a mane thing to say to any man." He added that it was hard to say from the accounts of the trial "whether Cap stole the dog."

He could gently ridicule the ado made about controversial episodes, as when Booker Washington was entertained at the White House, Mr. Dooley explained that when Booker was gone they counted the spoons. "They was all there. Booker had exercised gintilminly resthraint."

When I lived in Chicago there was a story of a letter of recommendation he wrote for an applicant for appointment to a place in the Court House. After the usual formal letter he added: "P.S. He's a good bye. He's fraquintly sober."

Other of his sayings were typical: "Hinnessy I've the judicial timpermint. I hate worruk." Also: Its the function of the Probate Court to see to it that "ivery mimber of the bar gets a fair chanst at fwhat the dicaysed couldn't take wid him."

When some day historians come to study the beginnings of a time of far-reaching change in American life, the philosophy of Martin Dooley will be a real factor in understanding them.

ROSCOE POUND

WORDS AND PHRASES by Mr. Dooley

ART OF ADVOCACY. If a lawyer thinks his client is innocint he talks to th' jury about th' crime. But if he knows where th' pris'ner hid th' plunder, he unfurls th' flag, throws out a few remarks about th' flowers an' th' bur-rds, an' asks th' twelve good men an' thrue not to break up a happy Chrismas, but to sind this man home to his wife an' childher, an' Gawd will bless thim if they ar-re iver caught in th' same perdicymint.

BLUE LAWS. 'Ye can't make laws f'r this community that wud suit a New England village,' he says, 'where,' he says, 'th' people ar-re too uncivilized to be immoral,' he says.

CAPITAL PUNISHMENT. I don't believe in capital punishment, Hinnissy, but 'twill niver be abolished while th' people injye it so much.

CHURCH AND STATE. Rellijon is a quare thing. Be itself it's all right. But sprinkle a little pollyticks into it an' dinnymite is bran flour compared with it. Alone it prepares a man f'r a better life. Combined with pollyticks it hurries him to it.

CLEAR AND PRESENT DANGER TEST. I'm sthrong f'r anny rivolution that ain't goin' to happen in me day.

CONSTITUTIONAL INTERPRETATION. ... th' constitootion iv th' United States is applicable on'y in such cases as it is applied to on account iv its applicability.

CRIMINAL LAW. In England a man is presoomed to be innocent till he's proved guilty an' they take it f'r granted he's guilty. In this counthry a man is presoomed to be guilty ontil he's proved guilty an' afther that he's presoomed to be innocent.

DECLARATION OF INDEPENDENCE. Th' constichooshion guarantees me th' right to life, but I die; to liberty, but if I thry bein' too free I'm locked up; an' to th' pursoot iv happiness, but happiness has th' right to run whin pursood, an' I've niver been able to tree her yet.

DE MINIMIS CURAT LEX [sic]. "Niver steal a dure-mat," said Mr. Dooley. "If ye do, ye'll be invistigated, hanged, an' maybe rayformed. Steal a bank, me boy, steal a bank."

DOMESTIC RELATIONS. Whin an ol' crazy-headed lunytic iv a woman skips out 'tis a crime; whin an ol' crazy-headed lunytic iv a duchess does it, it's a scandal; but whin an ol' crazy-headed lunytic iv a princess does it, it's a romance.

EQUAL PROTECTION OF THE LAW. . . . this home iv opporchunity where ivry man is th' equal iv ivry other man befure th' law if he isnt careful.

FREEDOM OF THE PRESS. If men cud on'y enjye th' wealth an' position th' newspapers give thim whin they're undher arrest! Don't anny but prominent clubman iver elope or embezzle?

HIGH FINANCE. 'Well,' says I, 'it ain't burglary, an' it ain't obtainin' money be false pretinses, an' it ain't manslaughter,' I says. 'It's what ye might call a judicious seliction fr'm th' best features iv thim ar-rts,' I says.

INDIGENT IN COURT. Don't I think a poor man

has a chanst in court? Iv coorse he has. He has the same chanst there that he has outside. He has a splendid poor man's chanst.

HUMAN FRAILTY. Thrust ivrybody—but cut th' cards.

INJUNCTIONS: I do not care who makes th' law iv a nation if I can get out an injunction.

INTERNATIONAL LAW. I will on'y say that hinceforth th' policy iv this gover'mint will be as befure not to bully a sthrong power or wrong a weak, but will remain thrue to th' principle iv wrongin' th' sthrong an' bullyin' th' weak.'

JUDICIAL TEMPERAMENT. "If I had me job to pick out," said Mr. Dooley, "I'd be a judge. I've looked over all th' others an' that's th' on'y wan that suits. I have th' judicyal timperamint. I hate wurruk.

JURY. In due time twelve men iv intilligence who have r-read th' pa-apers an' can't remimber what they've r-read, or who can't r-read, or ar-re out iv wurruk, ar-re injooced to sarve, an' th' awful wheels iv justice begins to go round.

Thank th' Lord, whin th' case is all over, th' jury'll pitch th' tistimony out iv th' window, an' consider three questions: 'Did Lootgert look as though he'd kill his wife? Did his wife look as though she ought to be kilt? Isn't it time we wint to supper?

LABOR LAW. Th' inthrests iv capital an' labor is th' same, wan thryin' to make capital out iv labor an' th' other thryin' to make laborin' men out iv capitalists.

LAW ENFORCEMENT. A polisman goes afther vice as an officer iv th' law an' comes away as a philosopher.

LAWS. 'I want a law,' he says, 'that mesilf an' all other good citizens can rayspict,' he says.

MARRIAGE AND DIVORCE. In me heart I think if people marry it ought to be f'r life. Th' laws ar-re altogether too lenient with thim.

MEDICO-LEGAL JURISPRUDENCE. "I wondher why ye can always read a doctor's bill an' ye niver can read his purscription."

POLICE POWER. A coort's all r-right enough, but no coort's anny good onless it is backed up be a continted constabulary, its counthry's pride, as th' pote says.

POLITICS. Whiniver I see an aldherman an' a banker walkin' down th' sthreet together I know th' Recordin' Angel will have to ordher another bottle iv ink.

PRECEDENTS. "Be hivins, Hinnissy, I want me advice up-to-date, an' whin Mack [McKinley] an' Willim Jennings tells me what George Wash'n'ton an Thomas Jefferson said, I says to thim: 'Gintlemen, they larned their thrade befure th' days iv open plumbin',' I says. 'Tell us what is wanted ye'ersilf or call in a journeyman who's wurrukin' card is dated this cinchry,' I says.

PRESIDENCY. A man expicts to be ilicted Prisidint iv th' United States, Hinnissy, f'r th' fine qualities that th' r-rest iv us use on'y to keep out iv th' pinitinchry.

PUBLIC POLICY. A Mormon, Hinnissy, is a man that has th' bad taste an' th' religion to do what a good manny other men ar-re restrained fr'm do-in' be conscientious scruples an' th' polis.

REFORM. But we're wan iv th' gr-reatest people in th' wurruld to clean house, an' th' way we like best to clean th' house is to burn it down.

REFORMER. A man that'd expict to thrain lobsters to fly in a year is called a loonytic; but a man that thinks men can be tur-rned into angels be an ilic-tion is called a rayformer an' remains at large.

REVERSING A LOWER COURT DECISION. ... f'r wan day th' other coort comes out an declares that th' decision of th' lower coort is another ar-gymint in favor iv abolishin' night law schools.

SENTENCING PROCEDURES. "There's on'y wan thing I can say in favor iv science." "What's that," asked Mr. Hennessy. "It's give us a good definse f'r our crimes," said Mr. Dooley. "F'r if we were started th' way th' Bible says we have wasted our opporchunities an' ought to be in jail; but if our ancesthors were what this scientist says they ar-re anny good lawyer cud get us off be pointin' out that with our bringin' up it's a miracle we ain't cannybals."

SUPREME COURT. It niver gives a decision till th' crowd has dispersed an' th' players have packed their bats in th' bags an' started f'r home.

[N]o matther whether th' constitution follows th' flag or not, th' supreme coort follows th' iliic-tion returns.

TRUSTS. The thrusts are heejous monsters built up be th' inlightened interprise iv th' men that have done so much to advance progress in our beloved counthry. On wan hand I wud stamp them undher foot; on th' other hand not so fast . . . Lave us laugh an' sing th' octupus out iv existence.

TRUTH. What we call thruth an' pass around fr'm hand to hand is on'y a kind iv a currency that we use f'r convenience. There are a good manny countherfeiters an' a lot iv th' countherfeits must be in circulation.

VICE-PRESIDENT. He must be a good speaker, a pleasant man with th' ladies, a fair boxer an' rassler, something iv a liar, an' if he's a Raypublican campaignin' in Texas, an active sprinter.

VOTER. Thousan's iv men who wudden't have voted f'r him undher anny circumstances has declared that under no circumstances wud they now vote f'r him.

WILLS. To be injyeable a will must be at wan an' th' same time a practical joke on th' heirs an' an advertisemint iv th' man that made it.

WOMEN'S RIGHTS. What does a woman want iv rights whin she has privileges?

MR. DOOLEY AT COURT

1. TRIAL PRACTICE—CIVIL AND UNCIVIL

On Criminal Trials

"Befure ye come in," said Mr. Dooley, "I was r-readin' in th' pa-aper a hard kick again th' delay between th' time a criminal bumps some wan an' th' time he gets th' bump that is comin' to him accordin' to th' law. This iditor feels bad because there's a diff'rence between this counthry an' England. Th' laws an' th' language ar-re th' same in th' two counthries but they're pronounced diff'rent. In England a man is presoomed to be innicent till he's proved guilty an' they take it f'r granted he's guilty. In this counthry a man is presoomed to be guilty ontil he's proved guilty an' afther that he's presoomed to be innicent.

"In th' oldher civilization th' judge reads th' news iv th' crime in th' mornin' pa-aper an' stops in at a hat shop on his way to coort an' buys a black cap to wear at th' approachin' fistivities. Whin he gets up on th' bench he calls th' shuriff to his side an' says he, 'Cap, go out an' grab a jury iv cross-lookin' marrid men to thry th' condimned.'

"Th' shuriff dhrags twelve indignant grocers fr'm their stores an' they come into coort protestin' because they will be bankrupted be sarvin' their counthry. But they ar-re soon restored to good humor be th' jovyal remarks iv th' coort, who makes him laugh heartily at wanst be askin' thim if they ar-re opposed to capital punishmint.

"Th' pris'ner is thin hauled in in chains, an' th' judge, afther exprissin' his dislike iv his face with a look iv scorn, says: 'Murdhrer, ye ar-re entitled to a fair thrile. Ar-re ye guilty or not guilty? Not guilty, ye say? I though ye wud. That's what th' good-f'r-nawthin' likes iv ye always says. Well, let's have this disagreeable business over with in a hurry. I'll allow th' prosecution three hours to show ye up an' th' definse can have th' rest iv th' mornin'. Wake me up whin th' evidence is all in.'

"About noon his honor is woke be a note fr'm th' jury askin' how long they ar-re goin' to be kept fr'm their dinner. He hauls th' black cap out iv th' handbox an' puttin' it on over his wig, says: 'Pris'ner at th' bar, it is now me awful jooty to lave ye'er fate to a British jury. I will not attimpt to infloonce thim in anny way. I will not take th' time to brush away th' foolish ividince put in ye'er definse.

"'Ye'er lawyers have done as well as they cud with nawthin' to go on. If anny iv th' jury believe ye innicent let them retire to their room an' discuss th' matther over a meal iv bread an' water while th' chops burn on th' kitchen stove an' their clerks ar-re disthributin' groceries free to th' neighborhood. But if they have been con-vinced be th' overwhelmin' mass iv ividince an' th' admirable argymints again ye, they do not need to lave th' box, but can signify their verdict be givin three hearty British cheers in which the coort will jine.' An' that's all there is to it.

"But it's betther in this home iv th' free, mind ye. Afther th' polis have made up their mind that none

iv thim did it, they may or may not grab th' criminal. It depinds on th' weather. But supposin' it's a
pleasant summer's day an' th' fugitive is in th' saloon nex' dure showin' th' revolver an' thryin' to
thrade in a silver candlestick f'r a dhrink, an' th' polis foorce ar-re bendin' ivry effort to apprehind him
an' ar-re combin' th' whole counthry f'r him, an' he
doesn't know where to turn, but goes into th' station an' registhers an' gets his key an' ordhers his
breakfast in th' cell an' gives a pair iv sugar tongs,
a dimon necklace, a dozen knives an' forks, his au-
tymatic an' other vallyables to th' sergeant to lock
up in th' safe, an' laves wurrud not to be called,
that's on'y th' beginnin' iv th' exercises.

"Th' first year or two he passes away delightfully,
havin' his pitchers took an' put in th' pa-apers an'
being' intherviewed while th' iditor iv th' Sob section sinds beautiful ladies out to describe his pretty
little flat full iv keepsakes an' talk with his wife.
But wan mornin' he wakes up an' gets th' pa-apers
an' there's hardly anny more mention iv him thin if
he was a meetin' iv th' Temperance league, or debate in congress, or a speech iv th' prisidint, or a
war in th' Philipeens, an' that disturbs him.

"He fires his press agent, sinds f'r his lawyer an'
demands a thrile. If th' fish ar-re not bitin' th' lawyer coaxes a judge to come into town, an wanst more
George Awfulperson becomes a prom'nint citizen
an' can read th' pa-apers without bein' disgusted at
th' way they fill their colyums with news about no-
bodies.

"Th' first six months iv th' thrile ar-re usually taken in gettin' a jury that will be fair to both sides, but more fair to wan side thin th' other. Th' state's attorney makes an effort to get twelve men who have no prejudices excipt a gin'ral opinyon that th' pris'ner is guilty. Th' lawyer f'r th' definse on'y askes that his client shall be thried by a jury iv his peers or worse, but wud compromise if all twelve were mimbers iv th' same lodge as himsilf. In due time twelve men iv intilligence who have r-read th' pa-apers an' can't remimber what they've r-read, or who can't r-read, or ar-re out iv wurruk, ar-re in-jooced to sarve, an' th' awful wheels iv justice be-gins to go round.

"Th' scene in th' coort is very beautiful an' touchin'. Th' pris'ner's wife rents a baby f'r th' win-ter an' sets where th' jury can see her whin her hus-band kicks her undher th' table an' she weeps. Th' table in front iv th' culprit is banked with flowers an' he comes into th' coort wearin' a geeranyum in his button-hole. Afther a picture iv th' august thri-bunal iv justice has been taken, th' dhread proce-dure proceeds. On th' first iv August th' prosecution succeeds in gettin' into th' record th' fact that such a person as th' victim iver lived in spite iv th' objic-tions iv th' definse on th' ground that it is imma-teeryal. Th' lawyer f'r th' definse objects to all th' questions an' whin th' coort overrules him he takes an exciption. That is as much as to say to th' judge: 'I'll make a jack iv ye in th' coort iv appeals.' On th' twintieth iv Decimber afther a severe cross-examination iv th' principal witness th' jury askes th' coort f'r a recess so they can lynch him.

"On th' fifteenth iv th' follow in' April th' tisty-mony iv th' definse is submitted. It is first that th' pris'ner is insane an' five profissors fr'm th' bean in-firmary swear that he was looney whin he done th' deed. Beside, he shot in self-definse, to protict his home an' th' honor iv American womanhood, while strugglin' with th' victim to keep him fr'm committin' suicide because th' pris'ner wudden't take his watch as a presint, th' gun accidintally wint off, a long an' a short man were seen leavin' th' premises afther th' crime, an' th' pris'ner was in Mitchigan City on that night, an' while on his way to see his sick child was stopped be an old lady who he res-cued fr'm drownin' in th' park, who gave him all she had in her purse, a forty-four, a jimmy, a brace an' bit, an' a quantity iv silverwear, clothing, curtains, an' joolry.

"So th' years roll brightly by an' day be day th' pris'ner sees his face on th' front page, th' fam'ly iv th' deceased is dhrove fr'm town be th' facts that has come out about his private life, an' most iv th' vallyable real estate in th' county is sold f'r taxes to pay th' bills iv th' short-hand writers f'r takin' down th' tistymony an' th' objictions iv th' definse. But though slow American justice, Hinnissy, is sure an' will overtake th' crim'nal if he'll on'y be patient an' not die, an' wan day all th' ividince is in. Th' dis-thrict attorney, who's a candydate f'r mayor, makes his closin' argymint, addhressin' th' jury as 'fellow

Republicans.' Th' lawyer f'r th' pris'ner askes th' jury on'y to consider th' law an' th' ividince an' to sind this innocent man home to his wife an' his starvin' childher.

"Afther th' judge has insthructed th' jury that he's all up in th' air about th' case an' doesn't know what he ought to say to thim, th' jury retires, charges its last meal to you, an' me an' discusses whether it ought to sind th' pris'ner home or some-where's else. Afther sindin' into coort an' gettin' a description iv his home they decide on temperin' justice with mercy an' find him guilty. Th' pris'ner is brought into coort, smilin' an' cheerful, th' flash-lights boom, th' cameras click, th' ladies swoon, an' th' judge says with a pleasant smile: 'It is me dhread jooty to sintince ye to th' Coort iv Appeals. Long life to ye.'

"Thin there's a lull in th' proceedin's. Th' seasons go swiftly by. Other things happen an' I can't re-mimber whether George Awfulperson was th' vic-tim iv th' crime, th' witness f'r th' prosecution, or th' disthrict attorney. Manny times has blithe spring turned to mellow summer. Manny times has autumn reddened th' threes in th' parks. Men that were old durin th' thrile ar-re dead. Men that were young ar-re old.

"Wan mornin' with decrepit fingers I open th' pa-aper an' r-read: 'Court iv Appeals revarses th' George Awfulperson case. Th' coort yisterdah afth-ernoon held a long session fr'm two to a quarther to three an' cleared th' calendar up to eighteen sivinty-

five be revarsin' th' lower coort f'r errors an'
ign'rance iv th' law in all th' cases appealed. In th'
George Awfulperson case th' decision is that while
th' pris'ner was undoubtedly guilty, th' lower coort
made a bobble be allowin' th' disthrict attorney to
open th' window an' expose th' pris'ner to a dhraft,
be not askin' Juryman Number Two whether he had
iver been in th' dhry goods business, and' be omitin'
a comma afther th' wurrud, "so" on page fifty-three
thousan' and sivin hundherd an' eighty in th' record.'

"An' th' pris'ner is brought back f'r a new thrile.
Th' new thrile is always hurrid. Th' iditors refuse
a requist fr'm th' pris'ner to sind around annywan
to report it, th' iliventh assistant district attorney
appears f'r th' state in spite iv th' law on child labor, th' witnesses ar-re all dead an' burrid, an' th' onforchnit crim'nal is turned out on a wurruld that
has f'rgotten him so completely that he can't aven
get a job as an actor on th' vowdyville stage."

"What happens to him if he hasn't got anny
money?" asked Mr. Hennessy.

"He might as well be in England," said Mr.
Dooley.

Cross-Examinations

Mr. Dooley put down his newspaper with the remark; "They cudden't get me into coort as a witness; no, sir, not if 't was to hang me best frind.

"'T is hard enough," he said, "with newspapers
an' cinsus officers an' th' mim'ry iv cab dhrivers to
live down ye'er past without bein' foorced to dhrill it

in a r-red coat an' with a brass band ahead befure
th' eyes iv th' multitood. I did it wanst; I'll do it no
more. Wanst I was summonsed to appear in th' high
temple iv justice where Timothy Duffy is th' presid-
in' janius, as Hogan says, to give me priceless tistymony as to whether th' plumbin' in Harrigan's
house was fitted to hold wather. 'T was me opinyon,
havin' had a handful iv thrumps I held in Harrigan's
parlor spiled be Lake Michigan dhroppin' through
th' ceilin', that said plumbin' was conthrary to th'
laws an' ordinances iv th' county iv Cook, State iv
Illinois, S.S. made an' provided an' th' oamo. I put on
a high hat an' a long-tailed coat an' left a man in
charge iv me business an' wint down to Halsted
Street an' swore to, as solemnly as I cud, knowin'
that Harrigan wudden't pay th' rent annyhow. An'
what come iv it? I was two minyits givin' me tistymony, an' two hours thryin' to convince th' hon'rable coort—a loafer be th' name iv Duffy—an' th' able
jury that I hadn't stolen th' shirt on me back fr'm
a laundhry wagon. Th' coort was goin' to confine me
in jail f'r life f'r contimpt, th' lawyer f'r th' definse
sthrongly intimated that I was in th' neighborhood
whin Charlie Ross was kidnapped an' th' jury ast to
be allowed to bring in a verdict iv manslaughter
again me without exthra pay. As I wint out iv th'
coort two or three women in large hats hissed me
an' a man at th' dure threatened me with an um-
brelly ontill I made a counther dimonsthration with
me foot. Justice, says ye? I tell ye Hogan's r-right
whin he says: 'Justice is blind.' Blind she is, an' deef

an' dumb an' has a wooden leg! Niver again will they dhraw me to a coort. I'll take th' rude justice iv a piece iv lead pipe without costs or th' r-right iv appeal.

"Here in th' pa-aper they'se a piece about a la-ad that had throuble with his vallay-"

"What's a vallay?" Mr. Hennessy interrupted.

"A vallay," Mr. Dooley explained, "is a retired English gintleman hired be millyionaires who ar-re goin' into bankruptcy to wear their clothes. Naked a millyionaire comes into th' wurruld an' naked his vallay laves him. Th' vallay's a kind iv a chambermaid that sees th' millyionaire doesn't go to wurruk in his night shirt an' r-reads his letters. I can't make out what all iv his jooties is. He rubs th' millyionaire's head an' rubbers on his love affairs, an afther awhile laves him an' goes to wurruk f'r a society pa-aper. 'T is an ol' sayin' iv Hogan's that no man is a hero to his vallay. That's thrue. The' vallay's th' hero.

"Well, this millyionaire I've been r-readin' about, he had a vallay, an' the vallay lost his eye wondher-in' who th' lady was, an' thin he dipped too sthrong into th' Floridy wather an' th' millyionaire bounced him. He fired him out. 'Lord Roland,' he says, 'go,' he says. 'We've lived too long together,' he says. 'People can't tell us apart, we stagger so much alike,' he says. 'I'm gettin' so used to ye that I have no fear iv ye,' he says. 'It was bad enough whin ye give me blue suspinders with me r-red pantaloons,' he says, 'but,' he says, 'whin I asked f'r an orange an' ye brought in th' boot-jack, I felt that we cud no longer assocyate on terms iv akequality,' he says. 'Ye'll have to go back to th' House iv Lords,' he says. An' he fired him out an' wudden't pay him a cint iv wages he owed him f'r th' rest iv his life. So Lord Roland sues him an' has him in coort.

"Th' millyionaire thrips in thinkin' to himsilf: 'Tis on'y a question iv whether I shall pay this jook what I promised him or what he ought to ixpict fr'm a millyionaire. Do I or do I not owe Lord Roland eighty-two dollars f'r curry-combin' me in th' nex' cinchry. I'll lave it to an intillygint jury iv honest Americans who have always buttoned their own shirts, an' r-right will conker an' I'll keep me money.'

"That's where he was wrong. He had th' same ex-peryence I had, except mine was a case iv plumbin' an' his wan iv personal decoration. Afther he ex-plained to th' jury that he didn't owe Lord Roland annything because his lordship got a dhroopin' eye fr'm dhrink an' frequently give him th' same collar evry week, he was tur-rned over to th' attorney f'r th' prosecution, who cross-examined him.

" 'We will pass over th' question iv ye'er financial relations with me client,' says th' distinguished bar-risther, 'an' come down to ye'er own private life. To begin with ar-re ye or ar-re ye not a man iv th' most dissolute morals?' 'Answer yes or no,' says th' coort. 'He admits it,' says th' lawyer. 'Ye were dhrunk in 1892?' 'I can't raymimber,' says th millyionaire. 'Put it down that he's always dhrunk,' says th' lawyer. 'Where did ye get ye'er money? Ye don't know? Th' jury will take note iv th' fact that he prob'bly stole it. Ye'er father is dead. Did ye kill him? I think so. Now that ye rayfuse to pay Lord Roland what's not comin' to him, how about ye'er wife?' 'My wife isn't in this case,' says th' prisoner. 'Th' divvle she isn't,' says th' coort. 'I want ye to know that ivrybody is in this case. We play no fav'rites. Whin th' clear sunlight iv American justice is tur-rned loose on a matther iv this charackter nawthin' can be hid. Go on an' tell us about ye'er wife. Th' coort wishes to know. Th' coort is human,' says he. 'Isn't it thrue,' says th' lawyer, 'that ye'er spouse is pettish an' disagreeable be nature an' that th' colors iv her hair ar-re not fast, an' that Lord Roland frequently peeked through th' dure an' seen ye talkin' to her? Answer me, ye fiend in human form, don't that lovely golden sheen upon her locks come out in th' wash? Tell me, monsther, tell th' hon'rable coort that's now leanin' eagerly over th' bar to catch ivry pint, tell th' jury that wud like to carry home s'ciety chit-chat to their own tired wives, tell this intelligint concoorse iv American citizens behind me an' th' gallant knights iv th' pen in fr-ront iv me waitin' to spread th' details to th' wurruld, tell me, ruffyian, is Hivin or Peroxide iv Hydhrogen th' author iv th' splendor? Is her complexion her own or fr'm day to day? Did ye iver see her befure ye were marrid, an' if so with whom? An' about th' other women Lord Roland saw ye with. Were they no betther thin they ought to be or not as good as they might have been.

I can't recall their names but ye might tell us who they ar-re. Give us their names. Dhrag th' wretched crathers fr'm their hidin' places in th' vowdyville theautres an' lave thim to sthand in th' clear sunlight iv American justice,' he says, 'an' be smirched,' he says.

"There was scarcely a dhry eye in th' coort whin th' larned counsel concluded. Th' ladies in th' audjeence applauded furyously as name afther name was brought forward. Th' judge said that he had the time iv his life, an' th' jury afther securin' clippin's iv th' prisoner's wife's hair rayturned a verdict findin' Mrs. Hard Gold guilty iv peroxide in th' first degree, without extenuatin' circumstances, an' added a rider recommendin' th' ladies Lord Roland seen with Hard Gold be tur-rned out iv their lodgin's. It was a gr-reat triumph for th' r-right. It shows that th' coorts iv our fair land will put down with a stern hand th' growin' peroxide vice an' that justice will find out evil doers—whin they ar-re women—if it has to take th' bandages off its eyes an' hide in a clothes closet."

"It serves th' man r-right f'r havin' wan iv thim vallays ar-round th' house," said Mr. Hennessy.

"Well, it shows that," said Mr. Dooley. "An' it shows th' disadvantages iv wealth. No wan cares to hear what Hogan calls: 'Th' short an' simple scandals iv th' poor.'"

On Criminals

"Lord bless my sowl," said Mr. Dooley, "childher is a gr-reat responsibility,—a gr-reat responsibility.

Whin I think iv it, I praise th' saints I niver was married, though I had opporchunities enough whin I was a young man; an' even now I have to wear me hat low whin I go down be Cologne Sthreet on account iv th' Widow Grogan. Jawn, that woman'll take me dead or alive. I wake up in a col' chill in th' middle iv th' night, dhreamin' iv her havin' me in her clutches.

"But that's not here or there, avick. I was r-readin' in th' pa-apers iv a lad be th' name iv Scanlan bein' sint down th' short r-road f'r near a lifetime; an' I minded th' first time I iver see him,—a bit iv a curly-haired boy that played tag around me place, an' 'd sing 'Blest Saint Joseph' with a smile on his face like an angel's. Who'll tell what makes wan man a thief an' another man a saint? I dinnaw. This here boy's father wurrked fr'm morn till night in th' mills, was at early mass Sundah mornin' befure th' alkalis lith th' candles, an niver knowed a month whin he failed his jooty. An his mother was a sweet-faced little woman, though fr'm th' County Kerry, that nursed th' sick an' waked th' dead, an' niver had a hard thought in her simple mind f'r anny iv Gawd's creatures. Poor sowl, she's dead now. May she rest in peace!

"He didn't git th' shtreak fr'm his father or fr'm his mother. His brothers an' sisters was as fine a lot as iver lived. But this la-ad Petey Scanlan growed up fr'm bein' a curly-haired angel f'r to be th' toughest villyun in th' r-road. What was it at all, at all? Sometimes I think they'se poison in th' life iv a big city. Th' flowers won't grow here no more thin they wud in a tannery, an' th' bur-rds have no song; an' th' childher iv dacint men an' women come up hard in th' mouth an' with their hands raised again their kind.

"Th' la-ad was th' scoorge iv th' polis. He was as quick as a cat an' as fierce as a tiger, an' I well ray-mimber him havin' laid out big Kelly that used to thravel this post,—'Whistlin'' Kelly that kep' us awake with imitations iv a mockin' bur-rd,—I well raymimber him scuttlin' up th' alley with a score iv polismin laborin' afther him, thryin' f'r a shot at him as he wint around th' bar-rns or undher th' thrucks. He slep' in th' coal-sheds afther that until th' poor ol' man cud square it with th' loot. But, whin he come out, ye cud see how his face had hard-ened an' his ways changed. He was as silent as an animal, with a sideways manner that watched ivry-thing. Right here in this place I seen him stand f'r a quarther iv an' hour, not seemin' to hear a dhrunk man abusin' him, an' thin lep out like a snake. We had to pry him loose.

"Th' ol' folks done th' best they cud with him. They hauled him out iv station an' jail an' bridwell. Wanst in a long while they'd dhrag him off to church with his head down: that was always afther he'd been sloughed up f'r wan thing or another. Between times th' polis give him his own side iv th' sthreet, an' on'y took him whin his back was tur-rned. Thin he'd go in the wagon with a mountain iv thim on top iv him, swayin' an' swearin' an' sthrikin' each other in their hurry to put him to sleep with their clubs.

"I mind well th' time he was first took to be settled f'r good. I heerd a noise in th' ya-ard, an' thin he come through th' place with his face dead gray an' his lips just a turn grayer. 'Where ar-re ye goin', Petey?' says I. 'I was jus' takin' a short cut home,' he says. In three minyits th' r-road was full iv polismin. They'd been a robbery down in Halsted Sthreet. A man that had a grocery sthore was stuck up, an' whin he fought was clubbed near to death; an' they'd r-run Scanlan through th' alleys to his father's house. That was as far as they'd go. They was enough iv thim to've kicked down th' little cottage with their heavy boots, but they knew he was standin' behind th' dure with th' big gun in his hand; an', though they was manny a good lad there, they was none that cared f'r that short odds.

"They talked an' palavered outside, an' telephoned th' chief iv polis, an' more pathrol wagons come up. Some was f'r settin' fire to th' buildin', but no wan moved ahead. Thin th' fr-ront dure opened, an' who shud come out but th' little mother. She was thin an' pale, an' she had her apron in her hands, pluckin' at it. 'Gintlemin,' she says, 'what is it ye want iv me?' she says. 'Liftinant Cassidy,' she says, ' 'tis sthrange f'r ye that I've knowed so long to make scandal iv me befure me neighbors,' she says. 'Mrs. Scanlan,' says he, 'we want th' boy. I'm sorry, ma'am, but he's mixed up in a bad scrape, an' we must have him,' he says. She made a curtsy to thim, an' wint indures.

'Twas less than a minyit befure she come out, cling-
in' to th' la-ad's ar-rm. 'He'll go,' she says. 'Thanks
be, though he's wild, they'se no crime on his head.
Is there, dear?' 'No,' says he, like th' game kid he is.
Wan iv th' polismin stharted to take hold iv him, but
th' la-ad pushed him back; an he wint to th' wagon
on his mother's ar-rm.

"And was he really innocent?" Mr. McKenna
asked.

"No," said Mr. Dooley. "But she niver knowed it.
Th' ol' man come home an' found her: she was settin' in a big chair with her apron in her hands an
th' picture iv th' la-ad in her lap."

On Expert Testimony

"Annything new?" said Mr. Hennessy, who had
been waiting patiently for Mr. Dooley to put down
his newspaper.

"I've been r-readin' th' tistimony iv th' Lootgert
case," said Mr. Dooley.

"What d'ye think iv it?"

"I think so," said Mr. Dooley.

"Think what?"

"How do I know?" said Mr. Dooley. "How do I
know what I think? I'm no combi-nation iv chemist,
doctor, osteologist, polisman, an' sausage-maker,
that I can give ye an opinion right off th' bat. A
man needs to be all iv thim things to detarmine
annything about a murdher trile in these days. This
shows how intilligent our methods is, as Hogan says.
A large German man is charged with puttin' his wife

away into a breakfas'-dish, an' he says he didn't do it. Th' on'y question, thin, is, Did or did not Alphonse Lootgert stick Mrs. L. into a vat, an' rayjooce her to a quick lunch? Am I right?"

"Ye ar-re," said Mr. Hennessy.

"That's simple enough. What th' coort ought to've done was to call him up, an' say: 'Lootgert, where's ye'er good woman?' If Lootgert cudden't tell, he ought to be hanged on gin'ral principles; f'r a man must keep his wife around th' house, an' whin she isn't there, it shows he's a poor provider. But, if Lootgert says, 'I don't know where me wife is,' the coort shud say: 'Go out, an' find her. If ye can't projooce her in a week, I'll fix ye.' An' let that be th' end iv it.

"But what do they do? They get Lootgert into coort an' stand him up befure a gang iv young rayporthers an' th' likes iv thim to make pitchers iv him. Thin they summon a jury composed iv poor, tired, sleepy expressmen an' tailors an' clerks. Thin they call in a profissor from a colledge. 'Profissor,' says th' lawyer f'r the State, 'I put it to ye if a wooden vat three hundherd an' sixty feet long, twenty-eight feet deep, an' sivinty-five feet wide, an' if three hundherd pounds iv caustic soda boiled, an' if th leg iv a guinea pig, an' ye said yestherday about bi-carbonate iv soda, an' if it washes up an' washes over, an' th' slimy, slippery stuff, an' if a false tooth or a lock iv hair or a jawbone or a goluf ball across th' cellar eleven feet nine inches— that is, two inches this way an' five gallons that?'

D—2

'I agree with ye intirely,' says th' profissor. 'I made lab'ratory experiments in an' ir'n basin, with bichloride iv gool, which I will call soup-stock, an' coal tar, which I will call ir'n filings. I mixed th' two over a hot fire, an' left in a cool place to harden. I thin packed it in ice, which I will call glue, an' rock-salt, which I will call fried eggs, an' obtained a dark, queer solution that is a cure f'r freckles, which I will call antimony or doughnuts or annything I blamed please.'

" 'But,' says th' lawyer f'r th' State, 'measurin' th' vat with gas,—an' I lave it to ye whether this is not th' on'y fair test,—an' supposin' that two feet acrost is akel to tin feet sideways, an' supposin' that a thick green an' hard substance, an' I daresay it wud; an' supposin' you may, takin' into account th' measure-mints,—twelve be eight,—th' vat bein' wound with twine six inches fr'm th' handle an' a rub iv th' green, thin ar-re not human teeth often found in counthry sausage?' 'In th' winter,' says th' profissor. 'But th' sisymoid bone is sometimes seen in th' fut, sometimes worn as a watch-charm. I took two sisymoid bones, which I will call poker dice, an' shook thim together in a cylinder, which I will call Fido, poored in a can iv milk, which I will call gum arabic, took two pounds iv rough-on-rats, which I rayfuse to call; but th' raysult is th' same.' Question be th' coort: 'Different?' Answer: 'Yis.' Th' coort: 'Th' same.' Be Misther McEwen: 'Whose bones?' Answer: 'Yis.' Be Misther Vincent: 'Will ye go to th' divvle?' Answer: 'It dissolves th' hair.'

"Now what I want to know is where th' jury gets off. What has that collection iv pure-minded pathrites to larn fr'm this here polite discussion, where no wan is so crool as to ask what anny wan else means? Thank th' Lord, whin th' case is all over, the jury'll pitch th' tistimony out iv th' window, an' consider three questions: 'Did Lootgert look as though he'd kill his wife? Did his wife look as though she ought to be kilt? Isn't it time we wint to supper?' An', howiver they answer, they'll be right, an' it'll make little diff'rence wan way or th' other. Th' German vote is too large an ignorant, annyhow."

On the Dreyfus Case

"I see be th' pa-apers," said Mr. Dooley, "that Col. Hinnery, th' man that sint me frind Cap. Dhry-fuss to th' cage, has moved on. I sup-pose they'll give th' Cap a new thrile now."

"I hope they won't," said Mr. Hennessy. "I don't know annything about it, but I think he's guilty. He's a Jew."

"Well," said Mr. Dooley, "Ye'er thoughts on this subject is inthrestin', but not conclusive, as Dorsey said to th' Pollack that thought he cud lick him. Ye have a r-right to ye'er opinyon, an' ye'll hold it annyhow, whether ye have a r-right to it or not. Like most iv ye'er fellow-citizens, ye start impartial. Ye don't know annything about th' case. If ye knew annything, ye'd not have an opinyon wan way or th' other. They'se niver been a matther come up in my time that th' American people was so sure about as they ar-re about th' Dhryfuss case. Th' Frinch ar-re not so sure, but they's not a polisman in this coun-thry that can't tell ye jus' where Dhry-fuss was whin th' remains iv th' poor girl was found. That's be-cause th' thrile was secret. If 'twas an open thrile, an' ye heerd th' tistimony, an' knew th' language, an' saw th' safe afther 'twas blown open, ye'd be puzzled, an' not care a rush whether Dhry-fuss was naked in a cage or takin' tay with his uncle at th' Benny Brith Club.

"I haven't made up me mind whether th' Cap done th' shootin' or not. He was certainly in th' neighbor-hood whin th' fire started, an' th' polis dug up quite a lot iv lead pipe in his back yard. But it's wan thing to sus-pect a man iv doin' a job an' another thing to prove that he didn't. Me frind Zola thinks he's in-nocint, an' he raised th' divvle at th' thrile. Whin th' judge come up on th' bench an' opined th' coort, Zola was settin' down below with th' lawyers. 'Let us proceed,' says th' impartial an' fair-minded judge, 'to th' thrile iv th' haynious monsther Cap Dhry-fuss,' he says. Up jumps Zola, an' says he in Frinch: 'Jackuse,' he says, which is a hell of a mane thing to say to anny man. An' they thrun him out. 'Judge,' says th' attorney f'r th' diffinse, 'an' gintle-men iv th' jury,' he says. 'Ye're a liar,' says th' judge. 'Cap, ye're guilty an' ye know it,' he says. 'Th' decision iv th' coort is that ye be put in a cage, an' sint to th' Divvle's own island f'r th' r-rest iv ye'er life,' he says. 'Let us pro-ceed to hearin' th' tisti-mony,' he says. 'Call all th' witnesses at wanst,' he says, 'an' lave thim have it out on th' flure,' he says. Be this time Zola has come back; an' he jumps up, an', says he, 'Jackuse,' he says. An' they thrun him out.

" 'Befure we go anny farther,' says th' lawyer f'r th' difinse, 'I wish to sarve notice that, whin this thrile is over, I intind,' he says, 'to wait outside,' he says, 'an' hammer th' hon'rable coort into an ome-let,' he says. 'With these few remarks I will close,' he says. 'Th' coort,' says th' judge, 'is always r-ready to defind th' honor iv France,' he says; 'an', if th' larned counsel will consint,' he says, 'to step up here f'r a minyit,' he says, 'th' coort'll put a sthrangle hold on him that'll not do him a bit iv good,' he says. 'Ah!' he says. 'Here's me ol' frind Pat th' Clam,' he says. 'Pat, what d'ye know about this case?' he says. 'None iv ye'er business,' says Pat. 'Answered like a man an' a sojer,' says th' coort. 'Jackuse,' says Zola fr'm th' dureway. An' they thrun him out. 'Call Col. Hinnery,' says th' coort. 'He ray-fuses to answer.' 'Good. Th' case is clear. Cap forged th' will. Th' coort will now adjourn f'r dools, an' all ladin' offi-cers iv th' ar-rmy not in disgrace already will assim-ble in jail, an' com-mit suicide,' he says. 'Jackuse,' says Zola, an' started f'r th' woods, pursued be his fellow-editors. He's off somewhere in a three now hollerin' 'Jackuse' at ivry wan that passes, sufferin' martyrdom f'r his counthry an' writin' now an' thin about it all.

"That's all I know about Cap Dhry-fuss' case, an' that's all anny man knows. Ye didn't know as much,

Hinnissy, till I told ye. I don't know whether Cap stole th' dog or not."

"What's he charged with?" Mr. Hennessy asked, in bewilderment.

"I'll niver tell ye," said Mr. Dooley, "It's too much to ask."

"Well, annyhow," said Mr. Hennessy, "he's guilty, ye can bet on that."

Insanity as a Defense or the M'Naghten Rule in a Nutshell

Note. — For actual use of the "brainstorm" theory of insanity in court, see in general Langford, The Murder of Stanford White, 1962.

"What's an expert witness?" asked Mr. Hennessy.

"An expert witness," said Mr. Dooley, "is a doctor that thinks a man must be crazy to be rich. That's thrue iv most iv us, but these doctors don't mean it th' way I do. Their theery is that annything th' rich do that ye want to do an' don't do is looney. As between two men with money, th' wan with most money is craziest.

"In th' old days if a man kilt another man he took three jumps fr'm th' scene iv th' disaster to th' north corrydor iv th' County Jail. That still goes f'r th' poor man. No wan has thried to rob him iv th' privilege won f'r him be his ancestors iv bein' quickly an' completely hanged.

"But suppose ye have a little iv th' useful with ye. Ye br-reak into Hogan's house some night sufferin' fr'm an incontrollable impulse to take his watch. Don't get mad, now. I'm on'y supposin' all this. Ye wudden't take his watch. He has no watch. Well, he's sound asleep. Ye give him a good crack on th' head so he won't be disturbed an' hook th' clock fr'm undher th' pillow. Th' next day ye're arristed.

"Th' pa-apers comes out with th' news: 'Haughty son iv wealthy fam'ly steals watch fr'm awful Hogan. Full account iv dhreadful career iv th' victim. Unwritten law to be invoked.' There's an article to show that anny wan has a right to take Hogan's watch, that he was not a proper man to have th' care iv a watch, annyhow, an' that ye done well to hook it. This is always th' first step to'rd securin' cold justice f'r th' rich.

"Finally, in ordher that th' law may be enfoorced without regard to persons, an expert witness is hired f'r ye.

"Th' thrile begins. Ye walk in with a quick, nervous sthride an' set th' watch be th' coort clock. 'Ar-re ye guilty or not guilty?' says th' clerk. 'Guilty an' glad iv it,' says ye're lawyer amid cheers an' hisses. 'Have ye th' watch with ye?' says th' coort. 'I have,' says th' prisoner, smilin' in his peculiar way. 'Lave me look at it,' says th' coort. 'I will not,' says th' pris'ner, puttin' it back into his pocket.

" 'How ar-re ye goin' to defind this crook?' says th' Judge.

" 'We ar-re goin' to prove that at th' time he committed this crime he was insane.' says th' lawyer.

" 'I object,' says th' State's attorney. 'It is not legal to inthrajooce evidence iv insanity 'till th' proper foundations is established. Th' defince must prove that th' pris'ner has money. How do we know he isn't broke like th' rest iv us.

"Th' coort—How much money have ye got?

"Th' pris'ner—Two million dollars, but I expect more.

"Th' coort—Objection overruled.

"Th' expert is called. 'Doctor, what expeeryence have ye had among th' head cures?' 'I have been f'r forty years in an asylum.' 'As guest or landlord?' 'As both.' 'Now doctor, I will ask you a question. Supposin' this pris'ner to be a man with a whole lot iv money, an' supposin' he went to this house on th' night in question, an' suppose it was snowin', an' suppose it wasn't, an suppose he turned fr'm th' right hand corner to th' left goin' upstairs, an' supposin' he wore a plug hat an' a pair iv skates, an' supposin' th' next day was Wednesday—'

"'I objict,' says th' State's attorney. 'Th' statues, with which me larned frind is no doubt familiar, though I be darned if he shows it, f'rbids th' mention iv th' days iv th' week.'

"'Scratch out Winsday an' substichoot four o'clock in Janooary,' says th' coort. 'Now, how does th' sentence r-read?'

"Th' next day was four o'clock in Janooary, an' supposin' th' amount iv money, an' supposin' ye haven't got a very large salary holdin' th' chair iv conniption fits at th' college, an' supposin' ye don't get a cent onless ye answer r-right, I ask ye, on th' night in question whin' th' pris'ner grabbed th' clock was he or was he not funny at th' roof?'

" 'I objict to th' form iv question,' says th' State's attorney. 'In th' eighth sintince I move to sthrike out th' wurrud 'and' as unconstitutional, unprofissyonal, an' conthry to th' laws iv evidence.'

" 'My Heaven, has my client no rights in this coort?' says th' other lawyer.

" 'Ye bet he has,' says th' coort. 'We'll sthrike out th' wurrud 'and' but we'll substichoot th' more proper wurrud 'aloofness'.'

' "Did ye see th' pris'ner afther his arrest?' 'I did.' "Where?' 'In th' pa-apers.' 'What was he doin'?' 'His back was tur-rned.' 'What did that indicate to ye?' 'That he had been sufferin' fr'm a variety iv tomaine excelsis—'

" 'Greek wurruds,' says th' coort. 'Latin an' Greek,' says th' expert. 'Pro-ceed,' says th' coort.

" 'I come to th' conclusion,' says th' expert, 'that th' man, when he hooked th' watch, was sufferin' fr'm a sudden tempest in his head, a sudden explosion as it were, a sudden I don't-know-what-th'-divvle-it-was, that kind iv wint off in his chimbley, like a storm at sea.'

" 'Was he in anny way bug befure th' crime?'

" 'Not a bit. He suffered fr'm warts whin a boy, which sometimes leads to bozimbral hoptocoli-ographophilloplutomania or what th' Germans call tantrums, but me gin-rall con-clusion was that he was perfectly sane all his life till this minnyit, an' that so much sanity wint to his head an' blew th' cover off.'

"Has he been sane iver since?' says th' lawyer.

" 'Ye'd betther have a care how ye answer that question, me boy,' says th' pris'ner, carelessly jingling th' loose change in his pocket.

" 'Sane,' says th' expert. 'Well I shud think he was. Why, I can hardly imagine how he stayed feather-headed long enough to take th' villan's joolry. Sane, says ye? I don't mean anny disrespect to th' coort or th' bar, but if ye gintlemen had half as much good brains in ye're head as he has, me distinguished frinds, ye'd not be wastin' ye're time here. There ain't a man in this counthry th' akel iv this gr-reat man. Talk about Dan'l Webster, he was an idyut compared with this joynt intelleck. No, Sir, he's a fine, thoughtful, able, magnificent specimen iv man an' has been iver since between twelve four an' twelve four-an'-a-half on that fatal night. An' a good fellow at that.'

" 'What d'ye propose to do to stand this here testymony off?' says th' judge.

" 'I propose,' says th' State's attorney, 'to prove be some rale experts, men who have earned their repytations be testifyin' eight ways fr'm th' jack in a dozen criminal cases, that so far fr'm bein' insane on this particklar night, this was th' on'y time that he was perfeckly sane.'

"I'm glad I was acquitted," said Mr. Hennessy, "but some of thim experts ar-re a bad lot. What's th' diff-rence between that kind iv tistymony an' perjury?"

"Ye pay ye're money an' take ye're choice," said Mr. Dooley.

Law and Lawyers

"Jawn," said Mr. Martin Dooley, slapping the newspaper down on the bar with a vicious shove, "I'm goin' for to raise a vig'lance comity."

"For what?" said Mr. McKenna. "To lynch Hinnissy's goat?"

"No, bedad," said Mr. Dooley, "Twud take more than a rope to break th' neck iv that ugly brute. Did ye iver feel th' spine iv him? More likely he's felt yours. 'Tis like a ba-ar iv iron, it is that. No, not Hinnissy's goat, but worse. I'd hang th' lawyers— hang thim on iviry tellygraph pole fr'm Brighton to th' rid bridge, so that th' road'd look like a lane in th' ould land afther th' pike man was up in '98, on'y they didn't have tillygraph poles in thim days, but sint their tillygrams be mail.

"Now, mind ye, now, Jawn, I'm not sayin' all lawyers deserved to be hanged, but they'd be no gr-reat har-rm done if they was all hanged. 'Tis like Mike Dorney whin Father Casey sint him to th' basemint to sample some ol' stuff he had there. They was in tin bottles on th' shelf an' 'twas so dark Dorney couldn't tell wan fr'm th' other. So what does he do but take a dhrink fr'm thim all, wan afther another, an' by gar he got th' whiskey, but he got catsup, howly wather, an' goose grease, too. So be th' lawyers. String thim all up, says I, an' if anny iv thim can prove an allibyi give him a Christian burial with th' rites iv th' church.

"A lawyer be nature is a crool, har-rd man. If they was no burglars they'd be no lawyers an' turn

about, without lawyers they'd be no need iv burglars. If they wasn't anny burglars they'd be no polisman an' without polisman they'd be no money in th'
saloon business.

"But it aint that, Jawn, mind ye, that sets me
again them. No, faith. Listen to me, Jawn. Las' week
that low loafer of a stitch-an' haul bow-legged Con-
nockman, Maddigan, th' tailor, whose father shov-
eled coal, bedad—or turf—f'r my folks in Ireland, he
up an' sues me f'r $8 f'r a vest. I ordhered th' vest,
thrue f'r ye, but whin I got it I sint it back. A nice
dacint man come in here f'r a gin fizz, an' whin I
wint to shake it, bedad, a button flew off th' vest an'
hit th' good man in th' eye an' like to blinded him.
I sint th' vest back with me complimints an' th' low
little Connock pup sues me before a Swede judge
down be Halsted street. No thrue Irishman'd take
th' case, an' Maddigan had a little Jew man to prosecute me. I had th' divvle's own difinse. I had down
ol' Brinnan—him they call Brinnan on th' moor—to
swear he saw me in New York th' day Maddigan sint th' vest, an' I had long Mike O'Donnell f'r
to testify that Maddigan give me th' vest f'r a
Chris'mas prisint, an' Boland, th' polisman, tould me
whin he got through a burglary case at Maxwell
street he'd come around an' swear 'twas me sold th'
vest to Maddigan an' that Maddigan was suspected
iv bein' Willie Tascott. Well, sir, I had th' tailor's
goose cooked an' no lie. I wint on th' stand an' tould
me story in a way, by gar, that brought tears to th'
eyes iv th' judge. Th' little Jew man sets down in

front and looks me all over, an' what d'ye think th'
insultin' wretch hur-rls at me? He sizes me up an'
says he: 'Mr. Dooley, where was ye on the night iv
May fourth?' What d'ye think iv him, Jawn, to put
that question to a dacint, modest American citizen
that tinds to his own business and pays his taxes?
Glory be to Gawd, I felt awake. Thinks I: 'He takes
me f'r th' white hor-rse.' By gar, 'tis no question to
put to anny man. If it made Fa-ather Dorney lape
out in th' Sacristy how th' 'ell was wan iv th' lambs
iv th' flock to hear it quietly?"

"And what did you do?" asked Mr. McKenna,
with deep interest.

"What did I do but catch th' Jew man on th' head
with th' mun-u'cipial ord'nances. An' th' Swede
judge he give th' case to Maddigan with costs an'
fined me tin dollars f'r contimpt iv coort. By dad,
I had to sind around f'r me cousin James Dooley f'r
to have th' fine remitted. Me cousin James Dooley
is th' Chief Justice iv Halsted Street, an' they
all take their hats off to him, ye can bet ye'er life on
that, Jawn, I'm tellin' ye. Well, sir, whin th' case
was over I looks around me f'r me witnesses to take
away, an' nayther hide n'r hair could I find iv thim
till I wint downstairs in th' saloon, an' there was
Brinnan puttin' on a false mustache an' Mike O'Donnell changin' coats with a thramp."

"That's all right," said Mr. McKenna, moving to
the door. "But you haven't answered the question,
'Where were you on the night of May 4?'"

Mr. McKenna dodged the angostura bottle, but
the lemon-squeezer hit him on the back.

Jury Service

"I haven't seen you lately," said Mr. McKenna.

"Sure," said Mr. Dooley, "I haven't had time to be colloguin' with th' likes iv you, Jawn, or wastin' me intellect on me own business. I've been tindin' to th' inthrists iv me counthry an' ladlin' out justice be th' bucketful. I've been on a jury."

"If you'd asked me, I'd got you off," said Mr. McKenna.

"Ye wud not, thin," retorted Mr. Dooley, sternly. "I'm a citizen iv this here town in good standin' an' I have me rights. Wan iv thim is to be dhragged down town to administer th' law an' I wint with a kind heart to it.

" 'Twas befure me ol' frind Hogan an' th' thrile was wan iv th' mos' momintyous that was iver known. 'Twas this way: A man named Schmidt, a German man, had wurruds with a Kerry man be th' name iv Darsey over a cow an' Darsey he tol' th' neighbers that Schmidt, this here German man, was so-an'-so an' this-an'-that an' Schmidt hired a lawyer be th' name iv Cassidy to bring suit. Darsey he got a German lawyer called Krootzmeyer f'r to defind him an' they took their corners an' called me an' ilivin other la-ads f'r to sittle th' matther. Th' charge was diclamation iv charakter."

"What's that you say?" asked Mr. McKenna.

"Why," said Mr. Dooley, "Schmidt swore Darsey attackted his charak-ter. Anyhow, 'twas a thrile f'r ye'er life. Cassidy argued 'twas a shame f'r even an Irishman to go around disthroyin th' charak-ter iv a dacint German an Krootzmeyer pointed out that it was a thrait iv th' race to be outspoken. Schmidt's witnesses were near all iv th' right sort an' they swore to prove what Darsey said an' Darsey had twinty German min f'r to prove that what Darsey said was thrue an' that Schmidt stole th' cow. Cassidy called Krootzmeyer a liar twict durin' th' thrile an' Krootzmeyer said whin he got through his argymint 'twas his intintion f'r to kick a hole through Cassidy. That looked fair enough, I thought, but th' coort, hish honor, Judge Hogan, said he'd fine thim both if ayether iv thim come to blows in th' room. 'I'll say this, though,' he wint on, 'that if th' gintleman does right he'll wait till he gets outside an' thin put th' books into his larned brother.' 'I'll note an' ixciption,' says Cassidy. 'If ye'er honor plaze 'tis not in th' breed iv Brother Krootzmeyer to muss me up ayether,' he says, 'accordin' to Coke or Queensberry, Blackstun or Bill Bradburn,' he says.

"They give us th' case in th' afthernoon an' we ma-arched out. I had me mind made up. Dorsey give me th' office durin' th' thrile an' I recognized him to be wan iv th' ...." here Mr. Dooley lowered his voice to a whisper.

"You don't say," said Mr. McKenna with a grin.

"But," said Mr. Dooley, "th' German was sthrong, too. He belonged to th' ...." (whispering).

"Glory be!" cried Mr. McKenna in amazement. "Is that so?"

"It is; an' 'twas a hard case to decide. I stuck be Darsey, though. We set down in th' room an' wan iv th' jurors says: 'Well, here we are. We have to have a foreman.' 'I sh'd say not,' says a man named McGuire. ' 'Tis too much like wurruk.' 'But,' says th' other man, 'I'm a profissional jury man,' he says, 'an' I know it. We've got to have a foreman.' We ilicted th' man to th' job, an' thin we had a vote on th' vardict. They was six votes f'r Darsey and five f'r Schmidt. One ol' man with a bald head voted f'r to con-vict th' lawyers, but he changed to my side whin I told him th' law. Well, we a-argyed it out, an' our side was th' sthronger. On th' nex' to th' last vote 'twas iliven to wan, an' th' wan was a little man with long whiskers. He shtud out brave f'r Schmidt. He'd have nawthin' else. 'Will ye be a fool all ye'er life?' says I. 'We'er ilivin to wan,' I says. 'Faith,' says he, 'I've lived all me life in a Swede ward,' he said. 'But,' says th' foreman, 'don't ye believe Schmidt stole th' cow?' 'Iv coorse,' says th' blockhead. 'But what th' divole did th' little lawyer stand th' lie f'r?' says he. 'Sure, if it'd been me I'd 've rolled him if 'twas in th' coort iv th' O'Donnells, lave alone Hogan's shop.' 'Ar-re ye goin' to keep us here all night?' said th' foreman. 'Divvle th' bit I care,' says th' lad. 'I'm not keepin' ye,' he says. 'Th' folks is out iv town, we're paid by th' day, an' I was wanst a night watchman an' cud sleep on th' top iv a pole.'

"Well, he was a stubborn man, but I knowed him years ago an' I'd heerd he was a bit of a ca-ard player, Jawn. 'Now look here,' says I. ''Tis no use keepin' us out iv bed all night, little man,' says I.

'I'll tell ye what I'll do,' I says. 'I'll play ye wan game iv sivin up,' I says. 'I have ye,' says he. An' we wint at it. At th' end iv th' third hand 'twas six-an'-six an' he give me th' cards to dale. Th' foreman made out a verdick f'r Darsey."

"How was that?" Mr. McKenna asked.

"Jawn," said Mr. Dooley solemnly, "in th' in-thrests iv law an' justice an' not to skin th' little man, but to up-hold th' constitution, I turned th' jack."

The Art of Advocacy

"No, sir, I wudden't know how to advise a young man, but I've often thought that if I had me life to live over again I'd be a lawyer. 'Tis a noble profis-syon. It's nobler now thin it used to be in th' old days whin a lawyer had to go into coort an' holler till he was hoorse to arn his fee. In thim times 'twas no sinycure, as Hogan says. If I had throuble with ye, ye hurrid off to wan lawyer an' I to another, an' th' next month we were down in th' coort room hearin' what th' larned counsel had to say about us. No matther how th' judge decided I got me money's worth whin me attorney shook his finger at ye an' alluded to th' fact that ye are a low-browed ruffyan with a squint in ye'er eye. Thin his remarks about me. What a good fellow I was; how I sacrificed me-silf f'r me frinds; as he told th' story iv me life he wept an' I wept too, although this was th' first I'd heerd iv it. I niver cud feel that he was doin' it f'r thirty dollars. An' thin whin he come to dhrag out th' authorities to support me! I wint to law with ye

D—3

because I was cross an' wasn't sure whether I cud lick ye in a rough-an-tumble fight, but, whin me lawyer begin to talk, I seen at wanst that I was in coort to perform a disagreeable jooty in th' inthrests iv civvylization an' humanity. Th' decisions were all on my side. Be hivens it looked as though they were all written with an eye to this partickler case. It didn't make anny diff'rence whether th' decision was about the capture iv fugitive slaves or consarvin' th' goold standard, it fitted onto my case as though it had been measured f'r it.

"D'ye raymimber Grogan? He was me lawyer in thim days whin I had wrongs that I didn't propose to have trampled on. I took thim to Grogan, an' Grogan presinted thim to th' coort. Dear me, but 'twas a threat to see an' hear him. He'd been a pedlar in his youth, an' ye cud hear his voice as far as th' Indyanny state line. Whin he talked to th' judge ye'd think he was hollerin' insthructions to a ship wrecked sailor against th' wind. I can see him now as he knelt on th' flure an' called Heaven to witness th' justice iv his cause, or stalked acrost th' room to where me opponent sat an' hissed in his ear, 'Polthroon!' Whin he spoke iv th' other lawyer as 'me larned brother' he done it in such a way that ye expected th' other lawyer to reach f'r a gun. An it wasn't all talkin' ayether. 'Twas th' hardest kind iv exercise. His arms were always in motion. He wud bate th' table with his fist till th' coort house thrembled. He wud shake his head till ye'd think he'd shake it off. If he was th' lawyer in a case of as-

sault an' batthry he'd punch himself in th' jaw an'
fall over a chair to show th' jury how it happened.
If 'twas a murdher thrile he'd pretind to shoot himself through th' heart an' sink to th' ground dead
with his head in a wastepaper basket an' his foot in
a juryman's lap. If 'twas a breach iv promise suit
he'd kneel on th' flure in front iv a juryman that
looked soft an' beg him to be his. There was no kind
iv acrobat that ye iver see in a circus that cud give
annything to Grogan. An' whin he'd filled th' air
with beautiful language an' baten th' coort room
furniture into slivers, he'd sink down in his chair
overcome be his emotions, with th' tears pourin'
fr'm his eyes, an' give ye th' wink fr'm behind his
han'kerchief.

"He was th' gr-reat man, an' whin th' likes iv him
were alive 'twas some fun goin' to law. But now,
mind ye, if ye consult a lawyer he receives ye in his
office, looks out iv th' window while ye're tellin' th'
story iv th' crool wrong done ye be ye'er neighbor,
taps his nose with his eyeglasses an' says: 'Ye have
a perfectly good case. I advise ye to do nawthin.
Ninety-four dollars, please. Oh, if ye insist on thryin' th' case, I'll sind the office boy over with ye. He
always riprisints th' firm in coort.

" 'Don't ye iver go into coort,' says I. 'What wud I
be doin' in a smelly coort room talkin' up to a man
that was me chief clerk last year? says he. 'No, sir,
th' law is a diff'rent profissyon fr'm what it was
whin Dan'l Webster an' Rufus Choate an' thim gas
bags used to make a mighty poor livin' be shoutin'

at judges that made less. Th' law to-day is not only a profissyon. It's a business. I made a bigger honoraryum last year consolidatin' th' glue inthrests that aftherwards wint into th' hands iv a receiver, which is me, thin Dan'l Webster iver thought was in th' goold mines iv th' wurruld. I can't promise to take a case f'r ye an' hoot me reasons f'r thinkin' ye'er right into th' ears iv a larned judge. I'm a poor speaker. But if iver ye want to do something that ye think ye oughtn't to do, come around to me an' I'll show ye how to do it,' says he.

"Tis a grand pro-fissyon. An' if a man's a lawyer he can be ivrything else. Whin we want a man to do annything in this counthry fr'm conductin' a war to runnin' a polis foorce, we hire a lawyer. Nearly all prisidints have been lawyers. All th' la-ads in th' cabinet are lawyers.

"Whin an admiral comes home fr'm bravin' th' terrors iv th' seas an' th' sthrange dhrinks iv foreign lands 'tis to a lawyer he reports. Whin a gin'ral has commanded our gallant army in th' Ph'lippens an' suffered many a savage thrust fr'm th' bolo an' th' Springfield Republicans, he comes home to injye th' greatest honor that a sojer can injye, th' honor iv reportin' to th' head iv th' army, a gallant warryor fr'm th' Yale law school. Th' on'y man in th' govermint that ain't a lawyer is Tiddy Rosenfelt himself. But he gets th' best legal advice there is goin'. He has a cabinet iv lawyers an' he consults thim an' they till him he's perfectly right. An' so he is. F'r what is done today is th' law tomorrow.

2. APPELLATE PRACTICE—SOME REBUTTABLE
PRESUMPTIONS OF MR. DOOLEY

The Law's Delays

"If I had me job to pick out," said Mr. Dooley, "I'd be a judge. I've looked over all th' others an' that's th' on'y wan that suits. I have th' judicyal timpera-mint. I hate wurruk.

"Ivrybody else is pushed an' hurrid in this tumul-chuse age. Th' business man has to get to th' bank befure it closes an' th' banker has to get there be-fure th' business man escapes, an' th' high-priced ac-tor has to kill off more gradyates iv th' school iv act-in' thin iver he did, an' th' night editions iv th' pa-apers comes out arlier ivry mornin'. All is rush an' worry. Kings an' imprors duck about their jooties like bellhops, th' pampered son iv luxury at Newport is thryin' f'r a mile a minyit in his autymobill an' th' on'y leisure class left in th' wurruld is th' judicyary. Mind ye, Hinnissy, I'm not sayin' annything again' thim. I won't dhrag th' joodicyal ermine in th' mud though I haven't noticed that manny iv thim lift it immodestly whin they takes th' pollytical crossing. I have th' high rayspict f'r th' job that's th' alterna-tive iv sixty days in jail. Besides, me boy, I invy thim.

"Somewhere a la-ad hits somewan on th' head with an axe or sinds him a bunch iv proosic acid done up to look like candy. Maybe he does an' may-be he don't; but annyhow that's what he's lagged f'r. Th' polis are in a hurry to get to th' pool-room befure th' flag falls in th' first race an' they carry th' case to th' gran' jury; th' gran' jury indicts him without a thought or a suspicion iv a har-rd feelin', th' judge takes his breakfast on th' bench to be there in time an' charges th' jury to be fair but not to f'rget th' man done it, an' th' jury rayturns a verdict iv guilty with three cheers an' a tiger. Th' pris'ner has hardly time to grab up his hat befure he's hauled off to his funeral obsequies, an' th' onprejudiced public feels happy about it. I don't believe in capital punishment, Hinnissy, but 'twill niver be abolished while th' people injye it so much. They're jus' squarin' thimsilves f'r th' rayvoltin' details whin wurrud comes that Judge Tamarack iv Opolis has granted a stay iv proceedin's. Stays iv pro-ceedin's is devices, Hinnissy, be which th' high coorts keep in form. 'Tis a lagal joke. I med it up. Says Judge Tamarack: 'I know very little about this case excipt what I've been tol' be th' larned counsel f'r th' dayfinse, an' I don't believe that, but I agree with Lord Coke in th' maxim that th' more haste th' less sleep. Therefore to all sheriff's, greetin': Fen jarrin' th' pris'ner till ye hear fr'm us.'

"So th' pris'ner waits an' dhreams he's a lightnin' rod an' th' public waits an' ivrybody waits. Th' high coort is busy in its way. Ivry two or three years it is discovered takin' a nap at a county seat in th' corn belt, an' it hands down a decision f'r th' defindant in a case f'r damages growin' out iv th' Shay rebillion. Then it dhrops off again. Th' judge that thried th' case retires to a well-arned job with a railroad comp'ny, th' jury has ceased to look f'r their pitchers in th' pa-apers an' th' insurance comp'nies insure young Cyanide's life f'r the lowest known premyum. Occasionally a judge iv th' coort iv appeals walkin' in his sleep meets another judge, an' they discuss matthers. 'How ar-re ye gettin' on with th' Cyanide case, judge?' 'I'm makin' fair headway, judge. I r-read part iv th' vardict iv th' coroner's jury las' year an' nex' month whin th' fishin' is over, I expict to look into th' indictment. 'Tis a puzzlin' case. Th' man is not guilty.' 'Well, good bye, judge; I'll see ye in a year or two. Lave me know how ye're gettin' on. Pleasant dhreams!' An' so they part. Th' higher up a coort is, th' less they see iv each other. Their office hours are fr'm a quarther to wan leap years. Ye take a lively lawyer that's wurruked twinty hours a day suin' sthreet railrood comp'nies an' boost him onto a high coort an' he can't think out iv a hammock. Th' more exalted what Hogan calls th' joodicyal station, th' more it's like a dormitory. Th' years rowl by an' th' tillygraft op'rator that's been expictin' to sind a rush tillygram through young Cyanide sees his ohms an' his volts mouldin' an' no wurrud comes fr'm th' coort iv appeals but th' murmur iv th' chief justice discussin' th' nullification theery. But wan day, th' decision is wafted down. 'Th' coort finds,' it says, 'that th' vardict was conthry to th' law an' th' ividince. We seen this fr'm th' first. It's as plain as th' nose on ye'er face. Th' judge was prejudiced an' th' jury was ignorant. Th' ividince wasn't sufficient to hang a cat.

We revarse th' decision an' ordher a new thrile that
full justice may be done. We cannot help remarkin'
at this time on th' croolty iv subjectin' this Unforch-
nit man to all these years iv torture an' imprison-
ment with a case again' him which we see at a glance
durin' th' Mexican war cud not shtand th' test iv th'
law.'

"But whin th' decision is carried to th' pris'ner,
th' warden says 'Who?' 'P. Cyanide,' says th' clark
iv th' coort. 'He's not here,' says th' warden. 'On
consultin' me books, I find a man iv that name left in
th' year sivinty-wan.' 'Did he escape?' 'In a sinse.
He's dead.'

"So, Hinnissy, I'd like to be a judge iv a high
coort, dhreamin' th' happy hours away. No hurry,
no sthrivin' afther immejet raysults, no sprintin', no
wan hollerin' 'Dooley J. hurry up with that ne
exeat,' or 'Dooley, hand down that opinyion befure
th' batthry gives out.' 'Tis th' thrue life iv aise an'
gintlemanly comfort. 'Tis wait till th' clouds rowl
by; 'tis time was meant for slaves; 'tis a long life an'
a happy wan. Like th' Shamrock II, th' coort acts
well in stays but can't run befure th' wind. A jury is
f'r hangin' ivry man, but th' high coort says: 'Ye
must die, but take ye'er time about it an' go out th'
way ye like.' If I wanted to keep me money so that
me gran'-childher might get it f'r their ol' age, I'd
appeal it to th' supreme coort. Oh, th' fine judge I'd
make, f'r I can sleep annywhere, an' I'm niver im-
patient f'r annywan to get his jooes."

"I don't see," said Mr. Hennessy, "why they have

anny juries. Why don't they thry ivry man before th' supreme coort an' have done with it?"

"I have a betther way than that," said Mr. Dooley. "Ye see they're wurrukin' on time now. I wondher if they wudden't sthep livelier if they were paid be th' piece."

The Big Fine

"That was a splendid fine they soaked Jawn D. with." said Mr. Dooley.

"What did they give him?" asked Mr. Hennessy.

"Twinty-nine millyon dollars," said Mr. Dooley.

"O, great," said Mr. Hennessy. "That's a grand fine. It's a gorjous fine. I can't hardly believe it."

"It's thrue, though," said Mr. Dooley. "Twinty-nine millyon dollars. Divvle th' cent less. I can't exactly make out what th' charge was that they arrested him on, but th' gin'ral idee is that Jawn D. was goin' around loaded up to th' guards with Standard Ile, exceedin' th' speed limit in acquirin' money an' singin': 'A charge to keep I have,' till th' neighbors cud stand it no longer.

"Th' judge says: 'Ye're an old offender, an' I'll have to make an example iv ye. Twinty-nine millyon dollars or fifty-eight millyon days. Call th' next case, Mister Clerk.'

"Did he pay th' fine? He did not. Iv coorse he cud if he wanted to. He wudden't have to pawn annything to get th' money, ye can bet on that. All he'd have to do would be to put his hand down in his pocket, skin twinty-nine millyon dollar bills off iv his roll an' hurl thim at th' clerk.

"But he refused to pay as a matther iv principle. 'Twas not that he needed th' money. He don't care f'r money in th' passionate way that you an' me do, Hinnissy. Th' likes iv us are as crazy about a dollar as a man is about his child whin he has on'y wan. Th' chances are we'll spoil it.

"But Jawn D. having a large an' growin' fam'ly iv dollars, takes on'y a kind iv gin'ral inthrest in thim. He's issued a statement sayin' that he's a custojeen iv money appointed be himsilf. He looks afther his own money an' th' money iv other people. He takes it an' puts it where it won't hurt thim an' they won't spoil it. He's a kind iv a society f'r th' prevention iv croolty to money.

"If he finds a man misusing his money he takes it away fr'm him an' adopts it. Ivry Saturdah night he lets th' man see it f'r a few hours. An' he says he's surprised to find that whin, with th' purest intintions in th' wurruld, he is found thryin' to coax our little money to his home where it'll find conjannial surroundings an' have other money to play with, th' people thry to lynch him an' th' polis arrest him f'r abduction.

"So as a matther iv principle he appealed th' case. An appeal, Hinnissy, is where ye ask wan coort to show its contempt f'r another coort. 'Tis sthrange that all th' pathrites that have wanted to hang Willum Jennings Bryan an' mesilf f'r not showin' proper respect f'r th' joodicyary are now showin' their respect f'r th' joodicyary be appealin' fr'm their decisions.

"Ye'd think Jawn D. wud bow his head reverentially in th' awful presence iv Kenesaw Mt. Landis an' sob out: 'Thank ye'er honor. This here noble fine fills me with joy. But d'ye think ye give me enough? If agreeable I'd like to make it an even thirty millyons.' But he doesn't. He's like mesilf. Him an' me bows to th' decisions iv th' coorts on'y if they bow first.

"I have gr-reat respect f'r th' joodicyary, as fine a lot iv cross an' indignant men as ye'll find annywhere. I have th' same respect f'r thim that they have f'r each other. But I niver bow to a decision iv a judge onless, first, it's pleasant to me, an' second, other judges bow to it.

"Ye can't be too careful about what decisions ye bow to. A dec-cision that seems agreeable may turn out like an acquaintance ye scrape up at a picnic. Ye may be ashamed iv it tomorrah. Manny's th' time I've bowed to a decree iv a coort on'y to see it go up gayly to th' supreem coort, knock at th' dure an' be kicked down stairs be an angry old gintleman in a black silk petticoat. A decree iv th' coort has got to be pretty vinrable befure I do more than greet it with a pleasant smile.

"Me idea was whin I read about Jawn D.'s fine that he'd settle at wanst, payin' twinty-eight millyon dollars in millyon dollar bills an' th' other millyon in chicken-feed like ten thousand dollar bills, just to annoy th' clerk. But I ought to've known betther.

"Manny's th' time I've bent me proud neck to a de-

cision iv a coort that lasted no longer thin it took th'
lawyer f'r th' definse to call up another judge on th'
tillyphone. A judge listens to a case f'r days an'
hears, while he's figurin' a possible goluf score on
his blottin' pad, th' argymints iv two or three lawyers that no wan wud dare to offer a judgeship to.

"Ginrally speakin' judges are lawyers. They get
to be judges because they have what Hogan calls th'
joodicyal timpramint, which is why annybody gets
a job. Th' other kind iv people won't take a job.
They'd rather take a chance.

"Th' judge listens to a case f'r days an' decides it
th' way he intinded to. D'ye find th' larned counsel
that's just been beat climbin' up on th' bench an'
throwin' his arms around th' judge? Ye bet ye don't.
He gathers his law books into his arms, gives
th' magisthrate a look that manes: 'There's an elic-
tion next year,' an' runs down th' hall to another
judge. Th' other judge hears his kick an' says he:
'I don't know annything about this here case except
what ye've whispered to me, but I know me larned
collague, an' I wudden't thrust him to referee a
roller-skating contest. Don't pay th' fine till ye hear
fr'm me.'

"Th' on'y wan that bows to th' decision is th' fellow that won, an' pretty soon he sees he's made a
mistake, f'r wan day th' other coort comes out an'
declares that th' decision iv th' lower coort is another argymint in favor iv abolishing night law
schools.

"That's th' way Jawn D. felt about it an' he didn't

settle. I wondher will they put him away if he don't pay ivinchooly. 'Twill be a long sentence. A frind iv mine wanst got full iv kerosene an' attempted to juggle a polisman. They thried him whin he come out iv th' emergency hospital an' fined him a hundherd dollars. He didn't happen to have that amount with him at th' moment or at anny moment since th' day he was born. But th' judge was very lenient with him. He said he needn't pay if he cudden't. Th' coort wud give him a letter iv inthroduction to th' bridewell an' he cud stay there f'r two hundherd days.

"At that rate it'll be a long time befure Jawn D. an' me meet again on th' goluf-links. Hogan has it figured out that if Jawn D. refuses to go back on his puritan principles an' separate himsilf fr'm his money he'll be wan hundherd an' fifty-eight thousand years in cold storage. A man ought to be pretty good at th' lock step in a hundherd an' fifty-eight thousand years.

"Well, sir, glory be, but times has changed whin they land me gr-reat an' good frind with a fine that's about akel to three millyon dhrunk an' disorderly cases. 'Twud've been cheaper if he'd took to dhrink arly in life.

"I've made a vow, Hinnissy, niver to be very rich. I'd like to be a little rich, but not rich enough f'r annywan to notice that me pockets bulged. Time was whin I dhreamed iv havin' money an' lots iv it. 'Tis thrue I began me dhreams at th' wrong end. I spend th' money first in me dhreams an' thin I got it. I was always clear about th' way to spend it, but oncertain about th' way to get it.

"If th' Lord had intinded me to be a rich man he'd've turned me dhreams around an' made me clear about makin' th' money, but very awkward an' shy about gettin' rid iv it. There are two halves to ivry dollar. Wan is knowin' how to make it an' th' other is not knowin' how to spend it comfortably.

"When I hear iv a man with gr-reat business capacity I know he's got an akel amount iv spending incapacity. No matther how much he knew about business he wudden't be rich if he wasn't totally ignorant iv a science that we have developed as far as our means will allow.

"But now, I tell ye, I don't dhream iv bein' rich. I'm afraid iv it. In th' good old days th' polis coorts were crowded with th' poor. They weren't charged with poverty, iv coorse, but with th' results iv poverty, d'ye mind. Now, be hivens, th' rich have invaded even th' coorts an' th' bridewell. Manny a face wearin' side whickers an' goold rimmed specs peers fr'm th' windows iv th' black Maria. 'What's this man charged with?' says th' Coort. 'He was found in possession iv tin millyon dollars,' says th' polisman. An' th' judge puts on th' black cap."

"Well," said Mr. Hennessy, "'Tis time they got what was comin' to thim."

"I'll not say ye're wrong," said Mr. Dooley. "I see th' way me frind Jawn D. feels about it. He thinks he's doin' a great service to th' wurruld collectin' all th' money in sight. It might remain in incompetent hands if he didn't get it. 'Twud be a shame to lave it where it'd be misthreated.

"But th' on'y throuble with Jawn is that he don't see how th' other fellow feels about it. As a father iv about thirty dollars I want to bring thim up mesilf in me own foolish way. I may not do what's right be thim. I may be too indulgent with thim. Their home life may not be happy. Perhaps 'tis clear that if they wint to th' Rockyfellar institution f'r th' care iv money they'd be in betther surroundings, but whin Jawn thries to carry thim off I raise a cry iv 'Polis,' a mob iv people that niver had a dollar iv their own an' niver will have wan pounce on th' misguided man, th' polis pinch him an' th' governmint condemns th' institution an' lets out th' inmates an' a good manny iv thim go to th' bad."

"Dy'e ye think he'll iver sarve out his fine?" asked Mr. Hennessy.

"I don't know," said Mr. Dooley. "But if he does whin he comes out at th' end iv a hundherd and fifty-eight thousand years he'll find a great manny changes in men's hats an' th manes of transportation, but not much in annything else. He may find flyin' machines, but he'll see a good manny people still walking to their wurruk."

3. CONSTITUTIONAL LAW—MR. DOOLEY SPEAKS FOR THE SUPREME COURT

The Supreme Court's Decisions

"I see," said Mr. Dooley, "Th' supreme coort has decided th' constitution don't follow th' flag."

"Who said it did?" asked Mr. Hennessy.

"Some wan," said Mr. Dooley. "It happened a long time ago an' I don't raymimber clearly how it come up, but some fellow said that ivrywhere th' constitution wint, th' flag was sure to go. 'I don't believe wan wurrud iv it,' says th' other fellow. 'Ye can't make me think th' constitution is goin' thrapezin' around ivrywhere a young liftnant in th' ar-rmy takes it into his head to stick a flag pole. It's too old. It's a home-stayin' constitution with a blue coat with brass buttons onto it, an' it walks with a goold-headed cane. It's old an' it's feeble an' it prefers to set on th' front stoop an' amuse th' childher. It wudden't last a minyit in thim thropical climes. 'T wud get a pain in th' fourteenth amindmint an' die befure th' doctors cud get ar-round to cut it out. No, sir, we'll keep it with us, an' threat it tenderly without too much hard wurruk, an' whin it plays out entirely we'll give it dacint buryal an' incorp'rate oursilves under th' laws iv Noo Jarsey. That's what we'll do,' says he. 'But,' says th' other, 'if it wants to thravel, why not lave it?' 'But it don't want to.' 'I say it does.' 'How'll we find out?' 'We'll ask th' supreme coort. They'll know what's good f'r it.' "

"So it wint up to th' supreme coort. They'se wan thing about th' supreme coort, if ye lave annything to thim, ye lave it to thim. Ye don't get a check that entitles ye to call f'r it in an hour. The supreme coort iv th' United States ain't in anny hurry about catchin' th' mails. It don't have to make th' las' car. I'd back th' Aujitoroom again it anny day f'r a foot

race. If ye're lookin' f'r a game iv quick decisions an'
base hits, ye've got to hire another empire. It niver
gives a decision till th' crowd has dispersed an' th'
players have packed their bats in th' bags an' started
f'r home.

"F'r awhile ivrybody watched to see what th' supreme coort wud do. I knew mesilf I felt I cudden't
make another move in th' game till I heerd fr'm
thim. Buildin' op'rations was suspinded an' we sthud
wringin' our hands outside th' dure waitin' f'r information fr'm th' bedside. 'What're they doin'
now?' 'They just put th' argymints iv larned counsel in th' ice box an' th' chief justice is in a corner
writin' a pome. Brown J. an' Harlan J. is discussin'
th' condition iv th' Roman Empire befure th' fire.
Th' rest iv th' coort is considherin' th' question iv
whether they ought or ought not to wear ruchin' on
their skirts an' hopin' crinoline won't come in again.
No decision to-day?' An' so it wint f'r days, an'
weeks an' months. Th' men that had argyied that
th' constitution ought to shadow th' flag to all th'
tough resorts on th' Passyfic coast an' th' men that
argyied that th' flag was so lively that no constitution cud follow it an' survive, they died or lost their
jobs or wint back to Salem an' were f'rgotten. Ex-
pansionists contracted an' anti-expansionists blew
up an' little childher was born into th' wurruld an'
grew to manhood an' niver heerd iv Porther Ricky
except whin some wan get a job there. I'd about
made up me mind to thry an' put th' thing out iv me
thoughts an' go back to wurruk when I woke up wan

D—4

mornin' an' see be th' pa-aper that th' Supreme
Coort had warned th' constitution to lave th' flag
alone an' tind to its own business.

"That's what th' pa-aper says, but I've r-read over
th' decision an' I don't see annything iv th' kind
there. They'se not a wurrud about th' flag an' not
enough to tire ye about th' constitution. 'T is a matther iv limons, Hinnissy, that th' Supreme Coort has
been settin' on f'r this gineration—a cargo iv limons
sint fr'm Porther Ricky to some Eyetalian in Phily-
delphy. Th' decision was r-read be Brown J., him bein' th' las' justice to make up his mind, an' ox of
ficio, as Hogan says, th' first to speak, afther a crool
an' bitther contest. Says Brown J.: 'Th' question
here is wan iv such gr-reat importance that we've
been sthrugglin' over it iver since ye see us las' an'
on'y come to a decision (Fuller C.J., Gray J., Harlan J., Shiras J., McKenna J., White J., Brewer J.,
an' Peckham J. dissentin' fr'm me an' each other)
because iv th' hot weather comin' on. Wash'n'ton is
a dhreadful place in summer (Fuller C.J. dissentin').
Th' whole fabric iv our government is threatened,
th' lives iv our people an' th' pro-gress iv civilization
put to th' bad. Men are excited. But why? We ar-re
not. (Harlan J., "I am." Fuller C.J. dissentin', but
not f'r th' same reason.) This thing must be settled
wan way or th' other undher that dear ol' constitution be varchue iv which we are here an' ye ar-re
there an' Congress is out West practicin' law. Now
what does th' constitution say? We'll look it up
thoroughly whin we get through with this case (th'

rest iv th' coort dissentin'). In th' manetime we must be governed be th' ordnances iv th' Khan iv Beloochistan, th' laws iv Hinnery th' Eighth, th' opinyon iv Justice iv th' Peace Oscar Larson in th' case iv th' township iv Red Wing varsus Petersen, an' th' Dhred Scott decision. What do they say about limons? Nawthin' at all. Again we take th' Dhred Scott decision. This is wan iv th' worst I iver r-read. If I cudden't write a betther wan with blindhers on, I'd leap off th' bench. This horrible fluke iv a decision throws a gr-reat, an almost dazzlin' light on th' case. I will turn it off. (McKenna J. concurs, but thinks it ought to be blowed out.)   But where was I? I must put on me specs. Oh, about th' limons. Well, th' decision iv th' Coort (th' others dissentin') is as follows: First, that th' Disthrict iv Columbya is a state; second, that it is not; third, that New York is a state; fourth, that it is a crown colony; fifth, that all states ar-re states an' all territories ar-re territories in th' eyes iv other powers, but Gawd knows what they ar-re at home. In th' case iv Hogan varsus Mullins, th' decision is he must paper th' barn. (Hinnery VIII, sixteen, six, four, eleven.) In Wiggins varsus et al. th' cow belonged. (Louis XIV, 90 in rem.) In E. P. Vigore varsus Ad Lib., the custody iv th' childher. I'll now fall back a furlong or two in me chair, while me larned but misguided collagues r-read th' Histhry iv Iceland to show ye how wrong I am. But mind ye, what I've said goes. I let thim talk because it exercises their throats, but ye've heard all th' decision on this limon case that'll get into th' fourth reader.' A voice fr'm th' audjeence, 'Do I get me money back?' Brown J.: Who ar-re ye?' Th' Voice: 'Th' man that ownded th' limons.' Brown J.: 'I don't know.' (Gray J., White J., dissentin' an' th' r-rest iv th' birds concurrin' but f'r entirely diff'rent reasons.)

"An' there ye have th' decision, Hinnissy, that's shaken th' intellicts iv th' nation to their very foundations, or will if they thry to read it. 'Tis all r-right. Look it over some time. 'T is fine spoort if ye don't care f'r checkers. Some say it laves th' flag up in th' air an' some say that's where it laves th' constitution. Annyhow, somethin's in th' air. But there's wan thing I'm sure about."

"What's that?" asked Mr. Hennessy.

"That is," said Mr. Dooley, "no matther whether th' constitution follows th' flag or not, th' supreme coort follows th' iliction returns."

Colleges and Degrees—Justice at Yale

"I see," said Mr. Dooley, "that good ol' Yale, because it makes us feel so hale, dhrink her down, as Hogan says, has been cillybratin' her bicintinry."

"What's that?" asked Mr. Hennessy.

"'T is what," said Mr. Dooley, "if it happened to you or me or Saint Ignatyus Colledge'd be called our two hundherdth birthday. From th' Greek, bi, two, cintinry, hundherd, two hundherd. Do ye follow? 'Tis th' way to make a colledge wurrud. Think iv it in English, thin think it back into Greek, thin thranslate it. Two hundherd years ago, Yale Col-

ledge was founded be Eli Yale, an Englishman, an'
dead at that. He didn't know what he was doin' an
no more did I till I r-read iv these fistivities. I knew
it nestled undher th' ellums iv New Haven, Connecti-
cut, but I thought no more iv it thin that 't was th'
name iv a lock, a smokin' tobacco an' a large school
nestlin' undher th' ellums iv New Haven where ye
sint ye'er boy if ye cud affoord it an' be larned th'
Greek chorus an' th' American an' chased th' fleet,
fut ball an' th' more fleet aorist, a spoort that Hogan knows about, an' come out whin he had to an'
wint to wurruk. But, ye take me wurrud f'r it.
Yale's more thin that, Hinissy. I get it sthraight
fr'm th' thruthful sons iv Yale thimsilves that if it
hadn't been f'r this dear bunch iv dormitories nestlin' undher th' ellums iv New Haven, our beloved
counthry an' th' short end iv th' wurruld too, might
to-day be no betther thin they should be. Ivry great
invintion fr'm th' typewriter to th' V-shaped wedge
can be thraced to this prodigal instichoochion. But
f'r Yale, we'd be goin' to Europe on th' decks iv sail-
in' vessels instead iv comin' away in th' steerage iv
steamships or stayin' at home; we'd be dhrivin'
horses, as manny iv th' unlarned iv us do to this day
instead iv pushin' th' swift autymobill up hill; we'd
be writin' long an' amusin' letters to our frinds instead iv tillyphonin' or tillygraftin' thim. Listen to
what me classical assocyate Misther Justice Brewer,
iv th' supreme coort, '68—that was th' year he got
his ticket out—says about our alma mather.

" 'Two hundherd years ago,' he says, 'Yale had

sivin pro-fissors an' forty books; to-day she has
sivin hundherd pro-fissors an' near three hundherd
thousan' volumes iv lore. Annywan that takes an inthrest in these subjects can verify me remarks be
applyin' to th' janitor f'r th' keys. I am more con-
sarned with th' inflooence iv Yale on th' mateeryal
affairs iv th' wurruld. Whin this beautiful colledge
first begun to nestle undher th' ellums iv New Haven, ships were propilled be th' wind; our vehicles
were dhrawn be th' ox, th' horse, th' wife, th' camel,
th' goat, th' Newfoundland dog, th' zebra. Th' wind,'
he says, 'blows no more lustier now thin it did whin
Paul was tossed about th' Mediterranyan be th'
tumulchuse what's-its-name. Th' ox an' th' horse has
grown no sthronger, I assure ye, thin whin Abraham wint forth fr'm his father's house. But if Paul
was livin' today, he wud go to Rome be th' Rome an'
Tarsus thransportation line, first-class. I don't know
where he'd get th' money but he'd find it somewhere.
He'd go to Rome first-cabin an' whin he was in
Rome, he wud, as Prisidint Hadley's frind Cicero
wud say, do as th' Romans do. So be Abraham. Ye
can undherstand fr'm this brief sketch what Yale
has done. She has continyed to nestle undher th'
ellums iv New Haven an' th' whole face iv th'
wurruld has been changed. Ye will see th' value iv
nestlin'. I wud apply the method to thrusts. Iv all
th' gr-reat evils now threatenin' th' body politic an'
th' pollytical bodies, these crool organizations an'
combinations iv capital is perhaps th' best example
iv what upright an' arnest business men can do whin

they are let alone. They cannot be stamped out be laws or th' decisions iv coorts, if I have annything to say about it, or hos-tile ligislachion which is too frindly. Their desthruction cannot be accomplished be dimagogues. Miraboo, a Frinchman, wanst excited th' Frinch prolotoory to rayvolt. What good came iv it? They made France a raypublic, that's all. But something must be done about th' thrusts. They must be desthroyed or they must not. How to do it. Th' answer is found in th' histhry iv Yale. Whin steam was discovered, she was nestlin' undher th' ellums iv New Haven. Whin th' tillygraft was invinted, she nestled. She nestled two hundherd years ago. She is still nestlin'. I ask her sons to profit be th' example iv their almy mather an' nestle. Whin things go wrong, nestle. Whin th' counthry is alarmed, nestle. Do not attimpt to desthroy th' hateful thrusts with harsh laws or advarse ligislachion. Nestle. An' there are worse places to nestle in thin a good thrust. An' if ye feather th' nestle, it's aisier on ye.'

"Well, sir, I think 't was good advice, an' I'm sure, Hinnissy, that th' assimbled hayroes iv culture thought well iv their degrees whin they got thim. What's a degree, says ye? A degree is a certyficate fr'm a ladin' university entitlin' ye to wear a mother Hubbard in spite iv th' polis. It makes ye doctor iv something an' enables ye to practise at ye'er profission. I don't mind tellin' ye, Hinnissy, that if I was a law which I'm not, I'd have to be pretty sick befure I'd call in manny iv th' doctors iv laws I know, an' as f'r American Lithrachoor, it don't need a doctor so much as a coroner. But annyhow degrees is good things because they livils all ranks. Ivry public man is entitled ex-officio to all th' degrees there are. An' no public or private man escapes. Ye haven't got wan, ye say? Ye will though. Some day ye'll see a polisman fr'm th' University iv Chicago at th' dure an' ye'll hide undher th' bed. But he'll get ye an' haul ye out. Ye'll say: 'I haven't done annything,' an' he'll say: 'Ye'd betther come along quite. I'm sarvin' a degree on ye fr'm Prisidint Harper.' Some iv th' thriftier univarsities is makin' a degree th' alternytive iv a fine. Five dollars or doctor iv laws.

"They was manny handed out be Yale, an' to each man th' prisidint said a few wurruds explainin' why he got it, so's he'd know. I r-read all th' speeches: 'Kazoo Kazama, pro-fissor iv fan paintin' at th' Univarsity iv Tokeeo, because ye belong to an oldher civilization thin ours but are losin' it,' to 'Willum Beans, wanst iditor iv th' Atlantic Monthly but not now,' to 'Arthur Somerset Soanso who wrote manny long stories but some short,' to 'Markess Hikibomo Itto because he was around,' to 'Fedor Fedorvitch Fedorivinisky because he come so far.'

"An' thin they was gr-reat jubilation, an' shootin' off iv firewurruks an' pomes be ol' gradyates with th' docthors iv lithrachoor sittin' in th' ambulances waitin' f'r a hurry call. An' thin ivry wan wint home. I was glad to r-read about it, Hinnissy. It done me heart good to feel that boys must be boys even whin they're men. An' they'se manny things in th' wurruld that ye ought to believe even if ye think they're not so."

"D'ye think th' colledges has much to do with th' progress iv th' wurruld?" asked Mr. Hennessy.

"D'ye think," said Mr. Dooley, "t is th' mill that makes th' wather run?"

Women Suffrage—A Dissenting Opinion of Mr. Dooley

"Woman's Rights? What does a woman want iv rights whin she has priv'leges? Rights is th' last thing we get in this wurruld. They're th' nex' things to wrongs. They're wrongs tur-ned inside out. We have th' right to be sued f'r debt instead iv lettin' th bill run, which is a priv'lege. We have th' right to thrile be a jury iv our peers, a right to pay taxes an' a right to wurruk. None iv these things is anny good to me. They'se no fun in thim. All th' r-rights I in-jye I don't injye. I injye th' right to get money, but I niver have had anny money to spind. Th' consti-chooshion guarantees me th' right to life, but I die; to liberty, but if I thry bein' too free I'm locked up; an' to th' pursoot iv happiness, but happiness has th' right to run whin pursood, an' I've niver been able to three her yet. Here I am at iver-so-manny years iv age blown an' exhausted be th' chase, an' happiness is still able to do her hundherd yards in tin minyits flat whin I approach. I'd give all th' rights I read about for wan priv-lege. If I cud go to sleep th' minyit I go to bed I wudden't care who done me votin'.

"No, sir, a woman don't need rights. Th' pope, imprors, kings an' women have priv-leges; ordhin'ry men has rights. Ye niver hear iv th' Impror of Rooshya demandin' rights. He don't need thim in his wurruk. He gives thim, such as they ar're, to th' moojiks, or whativer it is ye call thim. D'ye think anny wan wud make a gr-reat success be goin' to th' Czar an' sayin': "Czar (or sire, as th' case may be), ye must be unhappy without th' sufferage. Ye must be achin' all over to go down to th' livry stable an' cast ye'er impeeral ballot f'r Oscaroviski K. Hickinski f'r school thrustee?" I think th' Czar wud reply: 'Gintlemen, ye do me too much honor. I mus' rayfuse. Th' manly art iv sufferage is wan iv th' most potint weepins iv th' freeman, but I'm not used to it, an' I wudden't know what to do with it. It might be loaded. I think I'll have to crawl along with me modest preerogatives iv collectin' th' taxes, dalin' life an' death to me subjicks, atin' free, dhrinkin' th' best an' livin' aisy. But ye shall have ye'er rights. Posicotofski, lade th' gintlemen out into th' coortyard an' give thim their rights as Rooshyan citizens. I think about twinty f'r each iv th' comity an' about a dozen exthry f'r the chairman. F'r wan iv th' rights guaranteed to his subjicks, be me sainted father, was a good latherin' ivry time it was comin' to thim.'

"An' so it is with women. They haven't th' right to vote, but they have th' priv'lege iv conthrollin' th' man ye ilict. They haven't th' right to make laws, but they have th' priv'lege iv breakin' thim, which is betther. They haven't th' right iv a fair thrile be a jury iv their peers; but they have th' priv'lege iv an unfair thrile be a jury iv their admirin' infeeryors. If I cud fly d'ye think I'd want to walk?"

Booker T. Washington, President Roosevelt, Mr. Dooley and the Fourteenth Amendment

"What ails th' prisidint havin' a coon to dinner at th' White House?" asked Mr. Hennessy.

"He's a larned man," said Mr. Dooley.

"He's a coon," said Mr. Hennessy.

"Well, annyhow," said Mr. Dooley, "it's goin' to be th' roonation iv Prisidint Tiddy's chances in th' South. Thousan's iv men who wudden't have voted f'r him undher anny circumstances has declared that under no circumstances wud they now vote f'r him. He's lost near ivry state in th' South. Th' gran' ol' commonwealth iv Texas has deserted th' banner iv th' raypublican party an Mississippi will cast her unanimous counted vote again him. Onless he can get support fr'm Matsachoosetts or some other state where th' people don't care annything about th' naygur excipt to dislike him, he'll be beat sure.

"I don't suppose he thought iv it whin he ast me cultured but swarthy frind Booker T. They'd been talkin' over th' race problem an' th' Cubian war, an' th' prospects iv th' race an' th' Cubian war, an' th' future iv th' naygro an' th' Cubian war, an' findin' Booker T. was inthrested in important public subjects like th' Cubian war, th' prisidint ast him to come up to th' White House an' ate dinner an' have a good long talk about th' Cubian war. 'Ye'll not be th' first Wash'nton that's et here,' he says. 'Th' other was no rilitive, or at laste,' says Booker T., 'he'd hardly own me,' he says. 'He might,' says th' prisidint, 'if ye'd been in th' neighborhood iv Mt. Vernon in his time,' he says. 'Annyhow,' he says, 'come up. I'm goin' to thry an experiment,' he says. 'I want to see will all th' pitchers iv th' prisidints befure Lincoln fall out iv th' frames whin ye come in,' he says. An' Booker wint. So wud I. So wud annywan. I'd go if I had to black up.

"I didn't hear that th' guest done annything wrong at th' table. Fr'm all I can larn, he hung his hat on th' rack an' used proper discrimination between th' knife an' th' fork an' ast f'r nawthin' that had to be sint out f'r. They was no mark on th' table cloth where his hands rested an' an invintory iv th' spoons after his departure showed that he had used gintlemanly resthraint. At th' con-clusion iv th' fistivities he wint away, lavin' his ilusthrees friend standin' on th' top iv San Joon hill an' thought no more about it. Th' ghost iv th' other Wash'nton didn't appear to break a soop tureen over his head. P'raps where George is he has to assocy-ate with manny mimbers iv th' Booker branch on terms iv akequality. I don't suppose they have par-titions up in th' other wurruld like th' kind they have in th' cars down south. They can't be anny Crow Hivin. I wondher how they keep up race su-preemacy. Maybe they get on without it. Anny-how I wasn't worrid about Booker T. I have me own share iv race prejudice, Hinnissy. Ne'er a man an' brother has darkened this threshold since I've had it or will but th' whitewasher. But I don't mind sayin' that I'd rather ate with a coon thin have wan wait on me. I'd sooner he'd handle his own food thin mine. F'r me, if anny thumb must be in th' gravy, lave it be white if ye please. But this wasn't my dinner an' it wasn't my house an' I hardly give it a thought.

"But it hit th' Sunny Southland. No part iv th' counthry can be more gloomy whin it thries thin th' Sunny Southland an' this here ivint sint a thrill iv horror through ivery newspaper fr'm th' Pattymack to th' Sugar Belt. 'Fr'm time immemoryal,' says wan paper I read, 'th' sacred rule at th' White House has been, whin it comes to dinner, please pass th' dark meat. It was a wise rule an' founded on thrue principles. Th' supreemacy iv th' white depinds on socyal supeeryority an' socyal supeeryority depinds on makin' th' coon ate in th' back iv th' house. He raises our food f'r us, cooks it, sets th' table an' brings in th' platter. We are liberal an' we make no attimpt to supplant him with more intilligent an' wage labor. We encourage his industhry because we know that f'r a low ordher iv intilligence, labor is th' on'y panacee. It is no good f'r a thoughtful man. We threat him right. He has plenty to do an' nawthin' to bother him an' if he isn't satisfied he be hanged. We are slowly givin him an' idjacation. Ivry year wan or more naygurs is given a good idjacation an' put on a north bound freight with a warnin'. But whin it comes to havin' him set down at th' table with us, we dhraw th' color line an' th' six shooter. Th' black has manny fine qualities. He is joyous, light-heated, an' aisily lynched. But as a fellow bong vivant, not be anny means. We have th' highest rayspict for Booker T. Wash'nton. He's an idjacated coon. He is said to undherstand Latin an' Greek. We do not know. But we know that to feed him at th' White House was an insult to ivry honest man an' fair woman in th' Sunny Southland an' a blow at white supreemacy. That must be avinged. Th' las' enthrinchmint iv socyal supeeryority in th' South is th' dinin' room an' there we will defind it with our sacred honor. We will not on'y defind our own dinin' room but ivry other man's, so that in time, if th' prisidint iv th' United States wants to ate with a naygur, he'll have to put on a coat iv burnt cork an' go to th' woodshed. Manetime we hear that th' white man in Alabama that voted f'r Rosenfelt las' year has come out again him. Th' tide has turned.'

"So there ye are. An' f'r th' life iv me, I can't tell which is right. But I think th' prisidint's place is a good dale like mine. I believe that manny an honest heart bates beneath a plaid vest, but I don't like a naygur. Howiver, Hinnissy, if Fate, as Hogan said, had condemned me to start in business on th' Levee, I'd sarve th' black man that put down th' money as quick as I wud th' white. I feel I wudden't, but I know I wud. But bein' that I'm up here in this Cowcasyan neighborhood, I spurn th' dark coin. They'se very little iv it annyhow an' if anny iv me proud customers was f'r to see an unshackled slave lanin' again this bar, it'd go hard with him an' with me. Me frinds has no care f'r race supeeryority. A raaly supeeryor race niver thinks iv that. But black an' white don't mix, Hinnissy' an' if it wint th' rounds that Dooley was handin' out rayfrishmint to th' colored popylation, I might as well change me license. So be th' prisidint. They'se nawthin' wrong in him havin' me frind Booker T. up to dinner. That's a fine naygur man, an' if me an' th' prisidint was in a private station, d'ye mind, we cud f'rget th' color iv th' good man an' say, 'Booker T. stretch ye'er legs in front iv th' fire, while I go to th' butcher's f'r a pound iv pork chops.' But bein' that I—an' th' prisidint—is public sarvants an' manny iv our customers has onrais'nable prejoodices, an' afther all 't is to thim I've got to look f'r me support, I put me hand on his shouldher an' says I: 'Me colored frind, I like ye an' ye're idjacation shows ye're a credit to th' South that it don't desarve, an' I wud swear black was white f'r ye; but swearin' it wudden't make it so, an' I know mos' iv me frinds thinks th' thirteenth amindmint stops at th' dure shtep, so if ye don't mind, I'll ast ye to leap through th' dure with ye'er hat on whin th' clock sthrikes sivin.' 'T is not me that speaks, Hinnissy, 't is th' job. Dooley th' plain citizen says, 'Come in, Rastus.' Dooley's job says: 'If ye come, th' r-rest will stay away.' An' I'd like to do something f'r th' naygur, too."

"What wud ye do?" asked Mr. Hennessy.

"Well," said Mr. Dooley, "I'd take away his right

to vote an' his right to ate at th' same table an' his right to ride on th' cars an' even his sacred right to wurruk. I'd take thim all away an' give him th' on'y right he needs nowadays in th' South."

"What's that?"

"Th' right to live," said Mr. Dooley. "If he cud start with that he might make something iv himsilf."

Freedom of the Press

A few years ago," said Mr. Dooley, "I thought that if I had a son I'd make a lawyer iv him. It was th' fine profission. Th' lawyers took all th' money an' held down all th' jobs. A lawyer got ye into throuble be makin' th' laws an' got ye out iv throuble be bustin' thim. Some lawyers on'y knew th' law, poor fellows, but others knew th' holes in th' law that made it as aisy f'r a millionaire to keep out iv th' pinitinchry as f'r a needle to enther th' camel's eye, as Hogan says. These lawyers niver had to worry about payin' their gas bills. A law, Hinnissy, that might look like a wall to you or me wud look like a thriumphal arch to th' expeeryenced eye iv a lawyer. Lawyers were ivrywhere, even on th' bench, be hivens. They were in th' ligislachure seein' that th' laws were badly punctuated an' in th' coorts seein' that they were thurly punctured. They were in Congress makin' th' laws an' th' flaws in th' laws. They r-run th' counthry. McKinley was a lawyer, Cleveland was a lawyer an' Bryan was a lawyer till he knew betther.

"But 'tis far diff'rent now, Hinnissy. If I had a

son 'tis little time I'd spind larnin' him what some dead Englishman thought Thomas Jefferson was goin' to mean whin he wrote th' Constitution. No, sir, whin me son an' heir was eight years old an' had r-read all th' best iv th' classical authors fr'm Deadwood Dick to Ol' Sleuth th' Detective I'd put a pencil in his hand an' shove him out into th' wurruld as a gr-reat iditor. I wud so. F'r th' lawyers ar-re too busy studyin' haby as corpus proceedin's to do annything else, an' 'tis th' Palajeem iv our Liberties that is runnin' th' counthry an' is goin' to run it f'r a long time to come.

"What's th' use iv a lawyer annyhow? If I get a good wan ye may hire a betther. Th' more money a man has th' betther lawyer he can get but th' more money a man has th' worse iditor he's liable to get. All anny lawyer can do is to holler at another lawyer. All a judge can do is to look unpleasant an' dhrop off into dhreams just at th' time whin th' most excitin' ividence in ye'er favor is bein' put in. No, sir, lawyers an' judges don't amount to annything. 'Tis th' twelve good men an' thrue dhragged fr'm butcher shop an' grocery store that decides. It's th' intillegent jury iv ye'er peers or worse that tells ye whether ye must put in th' rest iv ye'er days stickin' paper insoles into ready made shoes or wearin' out th' same lookin' f'r wurruk. Th' lawyers make th' law; th' judges make th' errors, but th' iditors make th' juries.

"So whin ye're landed down stairs in th' polis station an' ye sind f'r ye'er frinds ye say to thim: 'Boys,

ye needn't throuble ye'ersilf about what lawyer ye
get so long as he's cheap; but do ye go down to th'
iditor an' tell him that th' cause iv human freedom
is on thrile undher th' nom de ploom iv Malachi
Hinnissy,' says ye. An' whin ye come up f'r thrile
th' lawyer tells ye th' case looks bad f'r ye but he'll
thry to save ye; an' ye give him th' wink an' set serene f'r well ye know that ivry wan iv thim sworn
boolwarks iv justice facin' ye has been told ivry day
f'r two months that it is insanity but not crime to
steal a ham an' over th' honest heart iv each iv
thim is a copy iv the **Daily Kazoo** offerin' a season
ticket to th' baseball game to th' juror that gives th'
best reason why th' pop'law Malachi Hinnissy shud
be acquitted (Cut out this Coupon). An' afther th'
lawyers on both sides has pounded th' furniture to
pieces an' th' judge has read a little composition on
larceny fr'm th' third reader, th' jury gives a roar
iv 'not guilty' an' thin adjourns with th' judge, th'
bar an' th' pris'ner to th' office iv th' **Kazoo** to have
their pitchers taken. Ye put in th' next three weeks
writin' about ye'er sufferings an' afther that ye get
a good job as wan iv th' conthributors to th' fireside
frind. 'Th' thrile iv Luke McGlue as seen be Malachi
Hinnissy who was wanst acquitted iv stealin' a
ham.' 'Th' Hankerbilk Wedding Described be Hinnissy th' well known pork burglar.' 'A Night at th'
Theaytre be th' Notoryous Hinnissy.' 'What Hinnissy who Got Away With th' Ham Thinks iv Hinnery James.' Iv coorse ye'er career is short lived.
Th' fav'rites iv th' Foorth Estate, as Hogan says,

don't last long. Afther awhile ye'er place on th' staff is taken be some wan more desarvin'. Ye give way to th' Riv'rend Jefferson Petherson or Nan Pattherson. Th' column that ye wanst adorned is taken f'r th' cookin' receipts iv a lady just acquitted iv poisoning her husband. But ye've had ye'er good day an' if ye'd relied on a lawyer ye'd be settin' on th' side iv a road with thirty pounds iv hardware on ye'er ankles foolishly beatin' a lump iv rock with a hammer.

"That's what th' Press can do f'r thim it loves. But I like it betther f'r what it can hand to thim it don't love. Maybe th' iditor is onto ye. An' ye're arrested f'r lookin' longingly at a ham on Easter Sundah. Ye might as well go an' have ye'er hair cut an' save throuble f'r th' prison barber. Whin ye wake up in th' mornin' th' fam'ly newspaper comes in an' this is what ye see:

MURDERS HIS WIFE

F'R SURELY TH' SHOCK WILL KILL MRS. HINNISSY WHIN SHE HEARS HER HORRIBLE HUSBAND IS LOCKED UP F'R HOPIN' TO STEAL A HAM

"Th' thrile is set f'r Novimber but ye're thried, convicted an' doin' th' lock step last August if ye on'y knew it. Ivry night whin father comes home fr'm his wurruk he brings a copy iv th' **Kazoo** an' reads about this fiend in human form divine, which means you, Hinnissy. Ye'er horrid past leaps out in ivry saloon. People that niver heerd iv ye raymimber an' tell how ye robbed th' poor box, bate down a child with hip desease, starved ye'er fam'ly an' eloped with th' hired girl. Th' childher huddle together thremblin' at th' story iv ye'er life an' th' good woman sinds up a prayer that her boys may be saved fr'm timptation. Th' paper f'r th' home insists that larceny ought to be made a capital crime f'r ye'er binifit an' has what's called a sinposyum iv Christyan ministers at thirty dollars a sin demandin' th' enfoorcement iv th' unwritten law that allows anny man who rayspicts th' invioliability iv th' grocery store to commit murdher at sight. As th' thrile approaches citizens ar-re discovered thryin' to bribe th' coort clerk to put thim on th' jury. Th' journal iv th' fam'ly takes a pop'lar vote, none bein' illegible who ar-re not on th' jury list, an' ye're voted guilty be a majority iv two hundherd an' eight thousand to wan. Th' onscrupulous minority has to lave town on th' midnight thrain. Whin ye're taken over to th' coort th' polis has to dhraw guns to keep ye fr'm bein' torn to pieces be th' mob. Th' panel waitin' to be called to well an' thruly thry ye, hisses as ye pass an' a lady stabs ye with a hat pin. Siv'ral jurymen refuse to sarve because they have conscientious scruples against not hangin' ye. Ye thry to hide ye'er head behind a post but th' judge, who comes up f'r re-iliction in th' spring, sternly calls on ye to stand up while th' flash-light pitcher is bein' took. Two or three iv th' jurymen is on'y restrained be foorce fr'm attackin' ye while th' indictment is bein' read an' in about two minyits ye're joggin' over to th' thrain f'r Joliet an' ye'er frinds read in th' pa-aper:

"'TH' NOTORYOUS MISCREENT HINNISSY HAS GOT HIS JUST DUES THANKS TO AN IN-CORRUPTIBLE JURY IV CONSTANT READ-ERS IV THIS GUARJEEN IV POP'LAR RIGHTS. THERE WILL BE A DISTHRIBUTION IV TH' PRIZES TO TH' JURY OFFERED BE US AT FINUCANE'S HALL NEXT SUNDAH, WHIN TH' LARNED JUDGE DOUBHBOBY WILL MAKE TH' PRESINTATION SPEECH.'

"Wanst in a while a mistake is made. Maybe ye ain't guilty at all. Maybe 'tis found at th' thrile that ye were in Waukegan th' day th' crime was discov-ered an' it was another man iv th' same name that coveted th' ham. Th' Palajeem iv our Liberties does th' right thing be ye. Th' case demands a full, free, frank an' manly apology an' ye get it:

"We stated yisterdah that wan Hinnissy was convicted iv stealin' a ham. We regret to say this was not so. Adv.'

"Th' printed wurrud! What can I do against it? I can buy a gun to protect me against me inimy. I can change me name to save me fr'm th' gran' jury. But there's no escape f'r good man or bad fr'm th' printed wurrud. It follows me wheriver I go an' sthrikes me down in church, in me office, in me very home. There was me frind Jawn D. Three years ago he seemed insured against punishment ayether here or hereafther. A happy man, a relligous man. He had squared th' ligislachures, th' coorts, th' pollyticians

an' th' Baptist clargy. He saw th' dollars hoppin' out
iv ivry lamp chimbley in th' wurruld an' hurryin'
to'rd him. His heart was pure seein' that he had
niver done wrong save in th' way iv business. His
head was hairless but unbowed. Ivry Mondah mornin' I read iv him leadin' a chorus iv 'Onward Christyan sogers marchin' f'r th' stuff.' He was at peace
with th' wurruld, th' flesh, an' th' divvle. A good
man! What cud harm him? An' so it seemed he
might pro-ceed to th' grave whin, lo an behold, up
in his path leaps a lady with a pen in hand an' off
goes Jawn D. f'r th' tall timbers. A lady, mind ye,
dips a pen into an inkwell! there's an explosion an'
what's left iv Jawn D. an' his power wudden't
frighten crows away fr'm a corn field. Who's afraid
iv Rockyfeller now? Th' prisidint hits him a kick, a
counthry grand jury indicts him, a goluf caddy over-
charges him an' whin he comes back fr'm Europo he
has as many polismen to meet him on th' pier as Doc
Owens. A year ago, annybody wud take his money.
Now if he wanted to give it even to Chancellor Day
he'd have to meet him in a barn at midnight.

"No, sir, as Hogan says, I care not who makes th'
laws or th' money iv a counthry so long as I run th'
presses. Father Kelly was talkin' about it th' other
day. . . . 'Ye say it invades our privacy. But so does
th' polisman, on'y he carries a warrant an' th' press
nabs us f'r crimes that are too intilligent f'r th' polis
to understand. It rules be findin' out what th' people
want an' if they don't want annything it tells thim
what it wants thim to want it to tell thim. It's

against all tyrants but itsilf an' it has th' boldest iv thim crookin' th' knee to it. . . .

" 'Yes, sir,' says he, 'th' hand that rocks th' fountain pen is th' hand that rules th' wurruld. Th' press is f'r th' whole univarse what Mulligan was f'r his beat. He was th' best polisman an' th' worst I iver knew. He was a terror to evil doers whin he was sober an' a terror to ivrybody whin he was dhrunk. Martin, I dhrink to th' la-ads all over th' wurruld who use th' printer's ink. May they not put too much iv th' r-red stuff in it an' may it niver go to their heads.' "

"An' what did ye say to that?" asked Mr. Hennessy.

"I said 'twud niver hurt annybody's head whose heart was in th' right place," said Mr. Dooley.

On Property Rights

Note: This essay illustrates a point made by Justice Holmes in Hudson Water Co. v. McCarter, 209 U.S. 349 at 355: "All rights tend to declare themselves absolute to their logical extreme. Yet all in fact are limited by the neighborhood of principles of policy which are other than those on which the particular right is founded, and which become strong enough to hold their own when a certain point is reached. The limits set to property by other public interests present themselves as a branch of what is called the police power of the State."

It'll be a hard winther if we don't get coal," said Mr. Hennessy.

"What d'ye want with coal?" said Mr. Dooley. "Ye're a mos' unraisonable man. D'ye think ye can have all th' comforts iv life, an' that ye mus' make no sacryfice to uphold th' rights iv property? Ivrybody will have plinty iv fuel this winther. Th' rich can burn with indignation, thinkin' iv th' wrongs inflicted on capital, th' middle or middlin' class will be marchin' with th' milishy, an' th' poor can fight among thimsilves. Th' Bible, th' mantelpiece, th' plumbin', th' bill fr'm th' butcher, th' phottygraft album, mother's switch, an' th' dorg will all go into th' furnace. If ye say a man has money to burn, it'll mean he's too poor or too mean to get coal. As f'r me I can keep warrum be jus' thinkin' iv th' situation. I can get up th' circylation iv me blood principally in me neck be readin' what me frind th' outspoken, oft-spoken, janial, tolerant, truthful an' religious Prisidint Baer has to say. There's a thruly great man, th' first prisidint we have raaly had that come up to me idee iv what a prisidint ought to be. He's a gr-reat lithrachoor, a gr-reat dayfinder iv th' hearth again' hard coal, th' protictor iv chillblains an' croup, th' inimy iv prickly-heat an' arnicy. Listen, will ye, to what Baer, Ursa Major as Hogan calls him, has to say iv th' histhry iv th' wurruld an' th' ways iv Providence, as revealed to him wan day as he was readin' th' scriptures on th' ticker:

"'Years ago,' says Baer, 'Nature decided that some day, afther sh'd had a long peeryod iv practise an' got her hand in be makin' th' stars, th' moon, th' sun, th' stock exchange, an' other divine wurruks, she'd compose me,' he says. 'It was no aisy task, an' she had to make a lot iv preparations f'r me arrival. There mus' be wurruk f'r me to do whin I come. At that peeryod, th' state iv Pinnsylvania, which was thin no state at all, was covered over with high threes, an' through these primevial forests stalked sthrange animals an' sthranger men. Wan day Nature bumped all th' trees over, knocked thim down with her mighty hand. "Why d'ye divastate th' land," she was ast. "I'm layin' it bare f'r Baer," says Nature with a jocose smile. Thin she shot thunder an' lightnin' down on th' popylation an' mingled its bones with th' threes. "Gunnin' f'r Baer," she says. An' she piled mud an' rock on th' timbers an' washed thim with th' floods an' cuked thim with fire an' left thim to cool, an' through long cinchries she wint fr'm time to time an' patted thim an' said: "Afther awhile a man with whiskers will come along an' claim ye. Don't laugh at him. That'll be Baer." Thin she mannyfactherd a lot of dilicate people that had to keep warrum or die an' she taught thim how to burn hard coal, an' thin I come. I call it Nature,' he says, 'but ye know who I mean. I am th' agent iv Divine Providence in this matther. All this coal was enthrusted to me be Hivin to look afther. Some say 'twas Morgan, but I know betther. I'm th' agent iv Providence — Providence Coal Comp'ny Limited, George Baer, agent. It's thrue I haven't made anny accountin' to me principal, but that'll come later. In th' manetime I stand as th' riprisintative iv visited inthrests, th' champeen iv ordher an' th' frind iv th' rights iv property. Gr-reat inthrests are at stake, as th' southern lyncher said at th' burnin'. I'm a wondherful man. An' funny, too,' he says.

"So what ar-re ye goin' to do about it? If thim

la-ads on'y got to own th' coal be th' same way that
I own th' part iv this house that ain't got a morgedge on it, an' ye own ye'er hat an' shoes—because
a lot iv fellows come together in th' ligislachoor an'
decided 'twas a good thing that a man who had
shoes an' a hat shud keep thim—'twud be diff'rent.
But seein' that th' Lord fixed it, there's nawthin' f'r
us to do but pray. Lave us pray that Hivin will go
out iv th' coal business, an' that it won't get into th'
Beef Thrust. I hate to think iv walkin' over to th'
stock yards to say me prayers.

"But I'm with th' rights iv property, d'ye mind.
Th' sacred rights an' th' divine rights. A man is
lucky to have five dollars; if it is ten, it is his jooty
to keep it if he can; if it's a hundherd, his right to it
is th' right iv silf-dayfinse; if it's a millyon, it's a
sacred right; if it's twinty millyon, it's a divine
right; if it's more thin that, it becomes ridickilous.
In anny case, it mus' be proticted. Nobody mus' in-
therfere with it or down comes th' constichoochion,
th' army, a letther fr'm Baer an' th' wrath iv Hivin.
If I own a house I can do what I plaze with it. I can
set fire to it anny time I want, can't I. Ye may have
foolish sintimints about it. Ye may say: 'If ye set
fire to ye'er house, ye'll burn mine.' But that don't
mine anny coal with me. 'Tis my house, give me in
thrust be th' Lord, an' here goes f'r a bonfire.
What's that fireman comin' down th' sthreet f'r?
How dare he squirt wather on me property? Down
with th' fire department! I've some gun powdher in
me cellar. I'll touch a match to it. I'm uncomfortable

in summer. I'll take me clothes off an' go f'r a walk. Th' sign above th' dure belongs to me. I'll loosen it so it will fall down on th' top iv ye'er head. Ye want to go to sleep at night. I'm goin' to have a brass band sur'nade me. I own a gun. I think I'll shoot me property into ye. Get out iv th' way f'r here comes property, dhrunk an' raisin' Cain. An' if I'm a sthriker with a stick iv dinnymite, I can explode it where an' whin I will. It happened to go off un-dher an' excursion thrain full iv women an childher. So much th' worse f'r thim, but they must be no re-sthriction on th' right iv a man to do what he will with his own. I ownded th' dinnymite an' I wanted to hear a noise. Hurrah f'r property rights! It's a gr-reat issue to lay befure th' American people whin th' coal gives out.'

"D'ye think th' sthrike 'll be settled? asked Mr. Hennessy.

"Iv coorse," said Mr. Dooley. "If it ain't, hell 'll break loose, an' we'll all be warrum.

MR. DOOLEY ON ADMINISTRATIVE LAW

Labor Relations

"I see th' sthrike has been called off," said Mr. Hennessy.

"Which wan?" asked Mr. Dooley. "I can't keep thrack iv thim. Somebody is sthrikin' all th' time. Wan day th' horseshoers are out, an another day th' teamsters. Th' Brotherhood iv Molasses Candy Pullers sthrikes, an' th' Amalgymated Union iv Pickle Sorters quits in sympathy. Th' carpinter that has been puttin' up a chicken coop f'r Hogan knocked off wurruk whin he found that Hogan was shavin' himsilf without a card fr'm th' Barbers' Union. Hogan fixed it with th' walkin' dillygate iv th' barbers, an' th' carpinter quit wurruk because he found that Hogan was wearin' a pair iv non-union pants. Hogan wint down-town an' had his pants unionized an' come home to find that th' carpinter had sthruck because Hogan's hens was layin' eggs without th' union label. Hogan injooced th' hens to jine th' union. But wan iv thim laid an egg two days in succission an' th' others sthruck, th' rule iv th' union bein' that no hen shall lay more eggs thin th' most reluctant hen in th' bunch.

"It's th' same ivrywhere. I haven't had a sandwich f'r a year because ivry time I've asked f'r wan aye-ther th' butchers or th' bakers has been out on sthrike. If I go down in a car in th' mornin' it's eight to wan I walk back at night. A man I knew had his uncle in th' house much longer than ayether iv thim

had intinded on account iv a sthrike iv th' Frindly
Brotherhood iv Morchuary Helpers. Afther they'd
got a permit fr'm th' walkin' dillygate an' th' remains was carrid away undher a profusyon iv floral
imblims with a union label on each iv thim, th' coort-
ege was stopped at ivry corner be a picket, who first
punched th' mourners an' thin examined their cre-
dintials. Me frind says to me: 'Uncle Bill wud've
been proud. He was very fond iv long fun'rals, an'
this was th' longest I iver attinded. It took eight
hours, an' was much more riochous goin' out thin
comin' back,' he says.

"It was diff'rent whin I was a young man, Hinnissy. In thim days Capital an' Labor were frindly,
or Labor was. Capital was like a father to Labor,
givin' it its boord an' lodgin's. Nayether inther-
fered with th' other. Capital wint on capitalizin', an'
Labor wint on laborin'. In thim goolden days a
wurrukin' man was an honest artisan. That's what
he was proud to be called. Th' week befure iliction
he had his pitcher in th' funny pa-apers. He wore a
square paper cap an' a leather apron, an' he had his
ar-rm ar-round Capital, a rosy binivolint old guy
with a plug-hat an' eye-glasses. They were goin' to
th' polls together to vote f'r simple old Capital.

"Capital an' Labor walked ar-rm in ar-rm instead
iv havin' both hands free as at prisint. Capital was
contint to be Capital, an' Labor was used to bein'
Labor. Capital come ar-round an' felt th' ar-rm iv
Labor wanst in a while, an' ivry year Mrs. Capital
called on Mrs. Labor an' congratylated her on her

score. Th' pride iv ivry artisan was to wurruk as long at his task as th' boss cud afford to pay th' gas bill. In return f'r his fidelity he got a turkey ivry year. At Chris'mas time Capital gathered his happy fam'ly around him, an' in th' prisince iv th' ladies iv th' neighborhood give thim a short oration. 'Me brave la-ads,' says he, 'we've had a good year. (Cheers.) I have made a millyon dollars. (Sinsation.) I atthribute this to me supeeryor skill, aided be ye'er arnest effort at th' bench an' at th' forge. (Sobs.) Ye have done so well that we won't need so manny iv us as we did. (Long an' continyous cheerin'.) Those iv us who can do two men's wurruk will remain, an', if possible, do four. Our other faithful sarvants,' he says, 'can come back in th' spring,' he says, 'if alive,' he says. An' th' bold artysans tossed their paper caps in th' air an' give three cheers f'r Capital. They wurruked till ol' age crept on thim, and thin retired to live on th' wish-bones an' kind wurruds they had accumylated.

"Nowadays 'tis far diff'rent. Th' unions has desthroyed all individjool effort. Year be year th' hours iv th' misguided wurrukin' man has been cut down, till now it takes a split-second watch to time him as he goes through th' day's wurruk. I have a gintleman plasthrer frind who tells me he hasn't put in a full day in a year. He goes to his desk ivry mornin' at tin an' sthrikes punchooly at iliven. 'Th' wrongs iv th' wurrukin' men mus' be redhressed,' says he. 'Ar-re ye inthrested in thim?' says I. 'Ye niver looked betther in ye'er life,' says I. 'I niver felt betther,' he says. 'It's th' out-iv-dure life,' he says. 'I haven't missed a baseball game this summer,' he says. 'But,' he says, 'I need exercise. I wish Labor Day wud come around. Th' boys has choose me to carry a life-size model iv th' Masonic Temple in th' parade,' he says.

"If I was a wurrukin' man I'd sigh f'r th' good ol' days, whin Labor an' Capital were frinds. Those who lived through thim did. In thim times th' arrystocracy iv labor was th' la-ads who r-run th' railroad injines. They were a proud race. It was a boast to have wan iv thim in a fam'ly. They niver sthruck. 'Twas again' their rules. They conferred with Capital. Capital used to weep over thim. Ivry wanst in a while a railroad prisidint wud grow red in th' face an' burst into song about thim. They were a body that th' nation might well be proud iv. If he had a son who asked f'r no betther fate, he wud ask f'r no betther fate f'r him thin to be a Brotherhood iv Locymotive Ingineers. Ivrybody looked up to thim, an' they looked down on ivrybody, but mostly on th' bricklayers. Th' bricklayers were niver bulwarks iv th' constichoochion. They niver conferred with Capital. Th' polis always arrived just as th' conference was beginnin'. Their motto was a long life an' a merry wan; a brick in th' hand is worth two on th' wall. They sthruck ivry time they thought iv it. They sthruck on th' slightest provocation, an' whin they weren't provoked at all. If a band wint by they climbed down th' laddhers an' followed it, carryin' banners with th' wurruds: 'Give us bread or we starve,' an' walked till they were almost hungry. Ivry Saturdah night they held a dance to protest again' their wrongs. In th' summer-time th' wails iv th' oppressed bricklayers wint up fr'm countless picnics. They sthruck in sympathy with annybody. Th' union wint out as wan man because they was a rumor that th' superintindent iv th' rollin'-mills was not nice to his wife. Wanst they sthruck because Poland was not free.

"What was th' raysult? Their unraisoning demands fin'lly enraged Capital. To-day ye can go into a bricklayer's house an' niver see a capitalist but th' bricklayer himsilf. Forty years ago a bricklayer was certain iv twelve hours wurruk a day, or two hours more thin a convicted burglar. To-day he has practically nawthin' to do, an' won't do that. They ar-re out iv wurruk nearly all th' time an' at th' seashore. Jus' as often as ye read 'Newport colony fillin' up,' ye read, 'Bricklayers sthrike again.' Ye very sildom see a bricklayer nowadays in th' city. They live mostly in th' counthry, an' on'y come into town to be bribed to go to wurruk. It wud pay anny man who is buildin' a house to sind thim what money he has be mail an' go live in a tent.

"An' all this time, how about th' arrystocracy iv labor, th knights iv th' throttle? Have they been deprived iv anny hours iv labor? On th' conthry, they have steadily increased, ontil to-day there is not a knight iv th' throttle who hasn't more hours iv wurruk in a day thin he can use in a week. In th' arly mornin', whin he takes his ir'n horse out iv th' stall, he meets th' onforchnit, misguided bricklayer comin' home in a cab fr'm a sthrike meetin'. Hardly a year passes that he can't say to his wife: 'Mother, I've had an increase.' 'In wages?' 'No, in hours.' It's th' old story iv th' ant an' th' grasshopper—th' ant that ye can step on an' th' grasshopper ye can't catch.

"Well, it's too bad that th' goolden days has passed, Hinnissy. Capital still pats Labor on th' back, but on'y with an axe. Labor rayfuses to be threated as a frind. It wants to be threated as an inimy. It thinks it gets more that way. They ar-re still a happy fam'ly, but it's more like an English fam'ly. They don't speak. What do I think iv it all? Ah, sure I don't know. I belong to th' onforchnit middle class. I wurruk hard, an' I have no money. They come in here undher me hospital roof, an' furnish thim with cards, checks, an' refrishmints. 'Let's play without a limit,' says Labor. 'It's Dooley's money.' 'Go as far as ye like with Dooley's money,' says Capital. 'What have ye got?' 'I've got a straight to Roosevelt,' says Labor. 'I've got ye beat,' says Capital. 'I've got a Supreme Court full of injunctions.' Manetime I've pawned me watch to pay f'r th' game, an' I have to go to th' joolry-store on th' corner to buy a pound iv beef or a scuttle iv coal. No wan iver sthrikes in sympathy with me."

"They ought to get together," said Mr. Hennessy.

"How cud they get anny closer together thin their prisint clinch?" asked Mr. Dooley. "They're so close together now that those that ar-re between thim ar-re crushed to death."

D—6

Immigration

"Well, I see Congress has got to wurruk again," said Mr. Dooley.

"The Lord save us fr'm harm," said Mr. Hennessy.

"Yes, sir," said Mr. Dooley, "Congress has got to wurruk again, an' manny things that seems important to a Congressman 'll be brought up befure thim. 'Tis sthrange that what's a big thing to a man in Wash'nton, Hinnissy, don't seem much account to me. Divvle a bit do I care whether they dig th' Nicaragoon Canal or cross th' Isthmus in a balloon; or whether th' Monroe docthrine is enfoorced or whether it ain't; or whether th' thrusts is abolished as Teddy Rosenfelt wud like to have thim or encouraged to go on with their neefaryous but magnificent entherprises as th' Prisidint wud like; or whether th' water is poured into th' ditches to reclaim th' arid lands iv th' West or th' money f'r thim to fertilize th' arid pocket-books iv th' conthractors; or whether th' Injun is threated like a depindant an' miserable thribesman or like a free an' indepindant dog; or whether we restore th' merchant marine to th' ocean or whether we lave it to restore itsilf. None iv these here questions inthrests me, an' be me I mane you an' be you I mane ivrybody. What we want to know is, ar-re we goin' to have coal enough in th' hod whin th' cold snap comes; will th' plumbin' hold out, an' will th' job last.

"But they'se wan question that Congress is goin' to take up that you an' me are intherested in. As a pilgrim father that missed th' first boats, I must raise me claryon voice again' th' invasion iv this fair land be th' paupers an' arnychists iv effete Europe. Ye bet I must—because I'm here first. 'Twas diff'-rent whin I was dashed high on th' stern an' rock-bound coast. In thim days America was th' refuge iv th' oppressed iv all th' wurruld. They cud come over here an' do a good job iv oppressin' thimsilves. As I told ye I come a little late. Th' Rosenfelts an' th' Lodges bate me be at laste a boat lenth, an' be th' time I got here they was stern an' rockbound thimsilves. So I got a gloryous rayciption as soon as I was towed off th' rocks. Th' stars an' sthripes whispered a welcome in th' breeze an' a shovel was thrust into me hand an' I was pushed into a sthreet excyvatin' as though I'd been born here. Th' pilgrim father who bossed th' job was a fine ol' puritan be th' name iv Doherty, who come over in th' May-flower about th' time iv th' potato rot in Wexford, an' he made me think they was a hole in th' break-wather iv th' haven iv refuge an' some iv th' wash iv th' seas iv opprission had got through. He was a stern an' rockbound la-ad himsilf, but I was a good hand at loose stones an' wan day—but I'll tell ye about that another time.

"Annyhow, I was rayceived with open arms that sometimes ended in a clinch. I was afraid I wasn't goin' to assimilate with th' airlyer pilgrim fathers an' th' instichoochions iv th' counthry, but I soon found that a long swing iv th' pick made me as good as another man an' it didn't require a gr-reat intel-lect, or sometimes anny at all, to vote th' dimmycrat

ticket, an' befure I was here a month, I felt enough
like a native born American to burn a witch. Wanst
in a while a mob iv intilligent collajeens, whose
grandfathers had bate me to th' dock, wud take a
shy at me Pathrick's Day procission or burn down
wan iv me churches, but they got tired iv that befure long; 'twas too much like wurruk.

"But as I tell ye, Hinnissy, 'tis diff'rent now. I
don't know why 'tis diff'rent but 'tis diff'rent. 'Tis
time we put our back again' th' open dure an' keep
out th' savage horde. If that cousin iv ye'ers expects
to cross, he'd betther tear f'r th' ship. In a few minyits th' gates 'll be down an' whin th' oppressed
wurruld comes hikin' acrost to th' haven iv refuge,
they'll do well to put a couplin' pin undher their
hats, f'r th' Goddess iv Liberty 'll meet thim at th'
dock with an axe in her hand. Congress is goin' to
fix it. Me frind Shaughnessy says so. He was in yisterdah an' says he: 'Tis time we done something to
make th' immigration laws sthronger,' says he.
'Thrue f'r ye, Miles Standish,' says I; 'but what wud
ye do?' 'I'd keep out th' offscourin's iv Europe,' says
he. 'Wud ye go back?' says I. 'Have ye'er joke,' says
he. ' 'Tis not so seeryus as it was befure ye come,'
says I. 'But what ar-re th' immygrants doin' that's
roonous to us?' I says. 'Well,' says he, 'they're
arnychists,' he says; 'they don't assymilate with th'
counthry,' he says. 'Maybe th' counthry's digestion
has gone wrong fr'm too much rich food,' says I;
'perhaps now if we'd lave off thryin' to digest
Rockyfellar an' thry a simple diet like Schwartz-

meister, we wudden't feel th' effects iv our vittels,'
I says. 'Maybe if we'd season th' immygrants a little
or cook thim thurly, they'd go down betther,' I says.

"They're arnychists, like Parsons,' he says. 'He
wud've been an immygrant if Texas hadn't been ad-
mitted to th' Union,' I says. 'Or Snolgosh,' he says.
'Has Mitchigan seceded?' I says. 'Or Gittoo,' he says.
'Who come fr'm th' effete monarchies iv Chicago,
west iv Ashland Av'noo,' I says. 'Or what's-his-
name, Wilkes Booth,' he says. 'I don't know what
he was—maybe a Boolgharyen,' says I. 'Well, annyhow,' says he, 'they're th' scum iv th' earth.' 'They
may be that,' says I; 'but we used to think they was
th' cream iv civilization,' I says. 'They're off th' top
annyhow. I wanst believed 'twas th' best men iv
Europe come here, th' la-ads that was too sthrong
and indepindant to be kicked around be a boorgo-
masther at home an' wanted to dig out f'r a place
where they cud get a chanst to make their way to
th' money. I see their sons fightin' into politics an'
their daughters tachin' young American idee how to
shoot too high in th' public school, an' I thought
they was all right. But I see I was wrong. Thim boys
out there towin' wan heavy foot afther th' other to
th' rowlin' mills is all arnychists. There's warrants
out f'r all names endin' in 'inski, an' I think I'll
board up me windows, f'r,' I says, 'if immygrants is
as dangerous to this counthry as ye an' I an' other
pilgrim fathers believe they are, they'se enough iv
thim sneaked in already to make us aborigines about
as infloointial as the prohibition vote in th' Twinty-

ninth Ward. They'll dash again' our stern an' rock-bound coast till they bust it,' says I.

"But I ain't so much afraid as ye ar-re. I'm not afraid iv me father an' I'm not afraid iv mesilf. An' I'm not afraid iv Schwartzmeister's father or Hinnery Cabin Lodge's grandfather. We all come over th' same way, an' if me ancestors were not what Hogan calls rigicides, 'twas not because they were not ready an' willin', on'y a king niver come their way. I don't believe in killin' kings, mesilf. I niver wud've sawed th' block off that curly-headed potintate that I see in th' pitchers down town, but, be hivins, Presarved Codfish Shaughnessy, if we'd begun a few years ago shuttin' out folks that wudden't mind handin' a bomb to a king, they wudden't be enough people in Mattsachoosetts to make a quorum f'r th' Anti-Impeeryal S'ciety,' says I. 'But what wud ye do with th' off-scourin' iv Europe?' says he. 'I'd scour thim some more,' says I.

"An so th' meetin' iv th' Plymouth Rock Assocyation come to an end. But if ye wud like to get it together, Deacon Hinnissy, to discuss th' immygration question, I'll sind out a hurry call f'r Schwartzmeister an' Mulcahey an' Ignacio Sbarbaro an' Nels Larsen an' Petrus Gooldvink, an' we'll gather tonight at Fanneilnoviski Hall at th' corner iv Sheridan an' Sigel sthreets. All th' pilgrim fathers is rayquested f'r to bring interpreters."

"Well," said Mr. Hennessy, "divvle th' bit I care, on'y I'm here first, an' I ought to have th' right to keep th' bus fr'm bein' overcrowded."

"Well," said Mr. Dooley, "as a pilgrim father on me gran' nephew's side, I don't know but ye're right. An' they'se wan sure way to keep thim out."

"What's that?" asked Mr. Hennessy.

"Teach thim all about our instichoochions befure they come," said Mr. Dooley.

Proposed: A Federal Divorce Law

"Well, sir," said Mr. Dooley, "I see they've been holdin' a Divoorce Congress."

"What's that?" asked Mr. Hennessy.

"Ye wudden't know," said Mr. Dooley. "Divoorce is th' on'y luxury supplied be th' law that we don't injye in Ar-rchey Road. Up here whin a marrid couple get to th' p'int where 'tis impossible f'r thim to go on livin' together they go on livin' together. They feel that way some mornin' in ivry month, but th' next day finds thim still glarin' at each other over th' ham an' eggs. No wife iver laves her husband while he has th' breath iv life in him, an' anny gin-tleman that took a thrip to Soo Falls in ordher to saw off th' housekeepin' expinses on a rash succes-sor wud find throuble ready f'r him whin he come back to Ar-rchey Road.

"'Tis th' fine skylark iv a timprary husband I'd make, bringin' home a new wife ivry Foorth iv July an' dischargin' th' old wan without a charakter. But th' customs iv th' neighbors are agin it.

"But tis diff'rent with others, Hinnissy. Down be Mitchigan Avnoo marredge is no more bindin' thin a dhream. A short marrid life an' an onhappy wan is their motto. Off with th' old love an' on with th' new an' off with that. Till death us do part, says th' preacher. 'Or th' jury,' whispers th' blushin' bride.

"Th' Divoorce Congress, Hinnissy, that I'm tellin' ye about was assembled to make th' laws iv all th' states on divoorce th' same. It's a tur-rble scandal as it is now. A man shakes his wife in wan State on'y to be grabbed be her an' led home th' minnyit he crosses th' border. There's no safety f'r anny wan. In some places it's almost impossible f'r a man to got rid iv his fam'ly onless he has a good raison. There's no regularity at all about it. In Kentucky baldness is grounds f'r divoorce, in Ohio th' inclemency iv th' weather. In Illinye a woman can be freed fr'm th' gallin' bonds iv mathrimony because her husband wears Congress gaiters; in Wisconsin th' old man can get his maiden name back because his wife tells fortunes in th' taycup. In Nebrasky th' shackles ar-re busted because father forgot to wipe his boots; in New York because mother knows a Judge in South Dakota.

"Ye can be divoorced f'r annything if ye know where to lodge th' complaint. Among th' grounds ar-re snorin', deefness, because wan iv th' par-ties dhrinks an' th' other doesn't, because wan don't dhrink an' th' other does, because they both drink, because th' husband is losin' his teeth, because th' wife is addicted to sick headaches, because he asked her what she did with that last $10 he gave her, be-

cause he knows some wan else, because she injyes th'
society iv th' young, because he f'rgot to wind th'
clock, because she wears a switch. A husband can
get a divoorce because he has more money thin he
had; a wife because he has less. Ye can always get
a divoorce f'r what Hogan calls incompatibility iv
timper. That's whin husband an' wife ar-re both
cross at th' same time. Ye'd call it a tiff in ye'er
fam'ly, Hinnissy.

"But, mind ye, none iv these reasons go in anny
two states. A man that wants to be properly divoorced so there's no danger whin he crosses th'
river at Cincinnaty that he'll have to wheel th' baby
carredge that give him his freedom will have to
start out an' do a tour iv our great Raypublic. An'
be th' time he's thurly released he may want to do it
all over again with th' second choice iv his wild glad
heart.

"It wud be a grand thing if it cud be straightened
out. Th' laws ought to be th' same ivrywhere. In
anny part iv this fair land iv ours it shud be th'
right iv anny man to get a divoorce, with alimony,
simply be goin' before a Justice of th' Peace an'
makin' an' affidavit that th' lady's face had grown
too bleak f'r his taste. Be Hivins, I'd go farther.
Rather than have people endure this sarvichood I'd
let anny man escape be jumpin' th' contract. All he
have to do if I was r-runnin' this Governmint wud
be to put some clothes in th' grip, write a note to his
wife that after thinkin' it over f'r forty years he had
made up his mind that his nature was not suited to

marredge with th' mother iv so manny iv his childer, an' go out to return no more.

"I don't know much about marrid life, except what ye tell me an what I r-read in th' papers. But it must be sad. All over this land onhappily mated couples ar-re sufferin' now an' thin almost as much as if they had a sliver in their thumb or a slight headache. Th' misfortunes of these people ar-re beyond belief. I say, Hinnissy, it is th' jooty iv th' law to marcifully release thim.

Ye take the case iv me frind fr'm Coke City that I was readin' about th' other day. There was a martyr f'r ye. Poor fellow! Me eyes filled with tears thinkin' about him. Whin a young man he marrid. He was a fireman in thim days, an' th' object iv his etarnal affection was th' daughter iv th' most popylar saloon keeper in town. A gr-reat socyal gulf opened between thim. He had fine prospects iv ivinchooly bein' promoted to two fifty a day, but, she was an heiress to a cellar full iv old rye an' a pool table, an' her parents objected, because iv th' difference in their positions. But love such as his was not to be denied. Th' bold suitor won. Together they eloped to Pittsburg an' were marrid.

"F'r a short time all wint well. They lived together happily f'r twenty years an' raised wan iv th' popylous fam'lies iv people who expect to be supported in their old days. Th' impechuse lover, spurred on be th' desire to make good with his queen, slugged, cheated, an' wurruked his way to th' head iv th' railroad. He was no longer Greasy Bill, th' Oil Can but Willum Aitch Bliggens, th' Prince iv Industhree. All th' diff'rent kinds iv money he iver heerd iv rolled into him, large money an' small, other people's money, money he'd labored f'r an' money he'd wished f'r. Whin he set in his office countin' it he often left a call f'r tin o'clock f'r fear he might be dhreamin' an not get to th' roundhouse on time.

"But, bein' an American citizen, he soon felt as sure iv himself as though he'd got it all in th' Probate Coort, an' th' arly Spring saw him in a private car speedin' to New York, th' home iv Mirth. He was rayceived with open ar-rms be ivry wan in that gr-reat city that knew the combynation iv th' safe. He was th' principal guest iv honor at a modest but tasteful dinner, where there was a large artificyal lake iv champagne into which th' comp'ny cud dive. He became th' prize package iv th' Waldorf.

"In th on'y part iv New York ye iver read about— ar-re there no churches or homes in New York, but on'y hotels, night restaurants, an' poolrooms? — in th' on'y part iv New York ye read about he cud be seen anny night sittin' where th' lights cud fall on his bald but youthful head. An little Angelica Gumdrop, th' lady next to th' end iv th' first row on th' right, looked on him with those big eyes iv hers that said so little an' meant so much.

"An' how was it all this time in dear old Coke City? It is painful to say that th' lady to whom our friend was tied f'r life had not kept pace with him. Shd had taught him to r-read, but he had gone on an' taken what Hogan calls th' post-grajate coorse. Women get all their book larnin' befure marredge, men afther. She'd been pretty active about th' childher while he was pickin' up more iddycation in th' way iv business than she'd iver dhream iv knowin'. She had th' latest news about th' throuble in the Methodist Church, but he had a private wire into his office.

"A life spint in nourishin' th' young, Hinnissy, while fine to read about, isn't anny kind iv a beauty restorer, an' I've got to tell ye that th' lady prob'bly looked dif'rent fr'm th' gazelle he used to whistle three times f'r whin he wint by on Number iliven. It's no easy thing to rock th' cradle with wan hand an' ondulate th' hair with another.

"Be th' time he was gettin' out iv th' sellin' class in New York she was slowin' down even f'r Coke City. Their tastes was decidedly dissimilar, says th' pa-aper. Time was whin he carrid th' wash pitcher down to th' corner f'r a quart iv malt, while she dandled th' baby an' fried th' round steak at th' same time. That day was past. She hadn't got to th' p'int where she cud dhrink champagne an' keep it out iv her nose. Th' passin' years had impaired all possible foundations f'r a new crop iv hair. Sometimes conversation lagged.

"Coke City (lovely haunt iv th' thrust as it is) is a long way fr'm th' Casino. Th' last successful exthravaganza that th' lady had seen was a lecture be Antiny Comstock. She got her Eyetalian opry out iv a music box. What was there f'r this joynt intelleck an' this household tyrant to talk about? No wonder he pined. Think iv this Light iv th' Tendherloin bein' compelled to set down ivry month or two an' chat about a new tooth that Hiven had just sint to a fam'ly up th' sthreet.

"Nor was that all. She give him no rest. Time an' time again she asked him was he comin' home that night. She tortured his proud spirit be recallin' th' time whin she used to flag him fr'm th' window iv th' room where Papa had locked her in. She even wint so far as to dhraw on him th' last cow'rdly weapon iv brutal wives—their tears. One time she thraveled to New York an' wan iv his friends seen her.

"Oh, it was crool, crool. Hinnissy, tell me, wud ye condim this gr-reat man to such a slavery just because he'd made a rash promise whin he didn't have a cent in th' wurruld? Th' law said no. Whin th' Gr-reat Financeer cud stand it no longer he called upon th' Judge to sthrike off th' chains an' make him a free man. He got a divoorce."

"I dare ye to come down to my house an' say thim things," said Mr. Hennessy.

"Oh, I know ye don't agree with me," said Mr. Dooley. "Nayther does Father Kelly. He's got it into his head that whin a man's marrid he's marrid, an' that's all there is to it. He puts his hand in th' grabbag an' pulls out a blank an' he don't get his money back. 'Ill-mated couples?' says he. 'Ill-mated couples? What ar-re ye talkin' about? Ar-re there anny other kinds? Ar-re there anny two people in th' wurruld that ar-re perfectly mated?' he says. 'Was there iver a frindship that was annything more thin a kind iv suspension bridge between quarrels?' he says. 'In ivry branch iv life,' says he, 'we leap fr'm scrap to scrap.'

" 'I'm wan iv th' best-timpered men in th' wurruld, am I not? (Ye are not,' says I.) I'm wan iv th' kindest iv mortals,' he says, 'but put me in th' same house with Saint Jerome,' he says, 'an' there'd be at laste wan day in th' month whin I'd answer his last wurrud be slammin' th' dure behind me,' he says.

" 'Man is nachurally a fightin' an' quarrelin' animal with his wife. Th' soft answer don't always turn away wrath. Sometimes it makes it worse,' he says. 'Th' throuble about divoorce is it always lets out iv th' bad bargain th' wan that made it bad. If I owned a half in a pavin' business with ye, I'd niver let th' sun go down on a quarrel,' he says. 'But if ye had a bad month I'd go into coort an' wriggle out iv th' partnership because ye're a cantankerous old villain that no wan cud get on with,' he says.

" 'If people knew they cudden't get away fr'm each other they'd settle down to life, just as I detarmined to like coal smoke whin I found th' collection wasn't big enough to put a new chimbley in th' parrish house. I've actually got to like it,' he says. 'There ain't anny condition iv human life that's not endurable if ye make up ye'er mind that ye've got to endure it,' he says.

" 'Th' throuble with th' rich,' he says, 'is this, that whin a rich man has a perfectly natural scrap with his beloved over breakfast, she stays at home an' does nawthin but think about it, an' he goes out an' does nawthin' but think about it, an' that afthernoon they're in their lawyers' office,' he says. 'But whin a poor gintleman an' a poor lady fall out, th' poor lady puts all her anger into rubbin' th' zinc off th' washboord an' th' poor gintleman aises his be murdhrin' a slag pile with a shovel, an' be th' time night comes ar-round he says to himsilf: "Well, I've got to go home annyhow, an' it's no use I shud be onhappy because I'm misjudged," an' he puts a pound iv candy into his coat pocket an' goes home an' finds her standin' at th' dure with a white apron on an' some new ruching around her neck,' he says.

"An' there ye ar-re. Two opinions."

"I see on'y wan," said Mr. Hennessy. "What do ye raaly think?"

"I think," said Mr. Dooley, "if people wanted to be divoorced I'd let thim, but I'd give th' childer th' custody iv th' parents. They'd larn thim to behave."

High Finance—Mr. Dooley before the S.E.C.

"I think," said Mr. Dooley. "I'll go down to th' stock yards an' buy a dhrove iv Steel an' **Wire** stock."

"Where wud ye keep it?" asked the unsuspecting Hennessy.

"I'll put it out on th' vacant lot," said Mr. Dooley, "an' lave it grow fat by atin' ol' bur-rd cages an' tin cans. I'll milk it hard, an' whin 'tis dhry I'll dispose iv it to th' widdies an' orphans iv th' Sixth Ward

that need household pets. Be hivins, if they give me
half a chanst, I'll be as gr-reat a fi-nanceer as anny
man in Wall sthreet.

"Th' reason I'm so confident iv th' value iv Steel
an' Wire stock, Hinnissy, is they're goin' to hur-rl
th' chairman iv th' comity into jail. That's what th'
pa-apers calls a ray iv hope in th' clouds iv dipres-
sion that've covered th' market so long. 'Tis always
a bull argymint. 'Snowplows common was up two
pints this mornin' on th' rumor that th' prisidint
was undher ar-rest.' 'They was a gr-reat bulge in
Lobster preferred caused be th' report that instoad
iv declarin' a dividend iv three hundhred per cint.
th' comp'ny was preparin' to imprison th' boord iv
directors.' 'We sthrongly ricommind th' purchase iv
Con and Founder. This comp'ny is in ixcillint condition since th' hangin' iv th' comity on reorganiza-
tion.'

"What's th' la-ad been doin', Hinnissy? He's been
lettin' his frinds in on th' groun' flure—an' dhroppin' thim into th' cellar. Ye know Cassidy, over in
th' Fifth, him that was in th' ligislachure? Well,
sir, he was a gr-reat frind iv this man. They met
down in Springfield whin th' la-ad had something he
wanted to get through that wud protect th' widdies
an' orphans iv th' counthry again their own avarice,
an' he must've handed Cassidy a good argymint, f'r
Cassidy voted f'r th' bill, though threatened with
lynchin' be stockholders iv th' rival comp'ny. He
come back here so covered with dimons that wan
night whin he was standin' on th' rollin' mill dock,

th' captain iv th' Eliza Brown mistook his shirt front f'r th' bridge lights an' steered into a soap fac-thry on th' lee or gas-house shore.

"Th' man made a sthrong impression on Cassidy. 'Twas: 'As me frind Jawn says,' or 'I'll ask Jawn about that,' or I'm goin' downtown to-day to find out what Jawn advises.' He used to play a dollar on th' horses or sivin-up f'r th' dhrinks, but afther he met Jawn he wanted me to put in a ticker, an' he wud set in here figurin' with a piece iv chalk on how high Wire'd go if hoopskirts come into fashion again. 'Give me a dhrop iv whisky,' he says, f'r I'm inthrested in Distillers,' he says, 'an I'd like to give it a shove,' he says. 'How's Gas?' he says. 'A little weak, today,' says I.' 'Twill be sthronger,' he says. 'If it ain't,' says I, 'I'll take out th' meter an' connect th' pipe with th' ventilator. I might as well bur-rn th' wind free as buy it,' I says.

"A couple iv weeks ago he see Jawn an' they had a long talk about it. 'Cassidy,' says Jawn, 'ye've been a good frind iv mine,' he says, 'an' I'd do annything in the wurruld f'r ye, no matther what it cost ye,' he says. 'If ye need a little money to tide over th' har-rd times till th' ligislachure meets again buy'— an' he whispered in Cassidy's ear. 'But,' he says, 'don't tell annywan. 'Tis a good thing, but I want to keep it bottled up,' he says.

"Thin Jawn took th' thrain an' begun confidin' his secret to a few select frinds. He give it to th' con-ductor on th' thrain, an' th' porther, an' th' candy butcher; he handed it to a switchman that got on

D—7

th' platform at South Bend, an' he stopped off at De-
troit long enough to tell about it to th' deepo' police-
man. He had a sign painted with th' tip on it an'
hung it out th' window, an' he found a man that
carrid a thrombone in a band goin' over to Buffalo,
an' he had him set th' good thing to music an' play
it through th' thrain. Whin he got to New York he
stopped at th' Waldorf Asthoria, an' while th' barber was powdhrin' his face with groun' dimons
Jawn tol' him to take th' money he was goin' to buy
a policy ticket with an' get in on th' good thing. He
tol' th' bootblack, th' waiter, th' man at th' news-
stand, th' clerk behind th' desk, an' th' bartinder in
his humble abode. He got up a stereopticon show
with pitchers iv a widow-an-orphan befure an'
afther wirin', an' he put an advertisement in all th'
pa-apers tellin' how his stock wud make weak men
sthrong. He had th' tip sarved hot in all th' res-
thrants in Wall sthreet, an' told it confidintially to
an open-air meetin' in Madison Square. 'They'se
nawthin,' he says, 'that does a tip so much good as
to give it circulation,' he says. 'I think, be this time,'
he says, 'all me frinds knows how to proceed, but—
Great Hivins!' he says. 'What have I done? Whin
all the poor people go to get th' stock they won't be
anny f'r thim. I can not lave thim thus in th' lurch.
Me reputation as a gintleman an' a fi-nanceer is at
stake,' he says. 'Rather than see these brave people
starvin' at th' dure f'r a morsel iv common or preferred, I'll—I'll sell thim me own stock,' he says. An'
he done it. He done it, Hinnissy, with unfalthrin'

courage an' a clear eye. He sold thim his stock, an' so's they might get what was left at a raysonable price, he wrote a confidintial note to th' pa-apers tellin' thim th' stock wasn't worth thirty cints a cord, an' now, be hivins, they're talkin' iv puttin' him in a common jail or pinitinchry preferred. Th' ingratichood iv man."

"But what about Cassidy?" Mr. Hennessy asked.

"Oh," said Mr. Dooley, "he was in here las' night. 'How's our old frind Jawn?' says I. He said nawthin'. 'Have ye seen ye'er collidge chum iv late?' says I. 'Don't mintion that ma-an's name,' says he. 'To think iv what I've done f'r him,' he says, 'an' him to throw me down,' he says. 'Did ye play th' tip?' says I. 'I did,' says he. 'How did ye come out?' says I. 'I haven't a cint lift but me renommynation f'r th' ligislachure,' says he. 'Well,' says I, 'Cassidy,' I says, 'ye've been up again what th' pa-apers call hawt finance,' I says. What th' divvle's that?' says he. 'Well,' says I, 'it ain't burglary, an' it ain't obtainin' money be false pretinses, an' it ain't manslaughter,' I says. 'It's what ye might call a judicious seliction fr'm th' best features iv thim ar-rts,' I says. 'Twas too sthrong f'r me,' he says. 'It was,' says I. 'Ye're about up to simple thransom climbin', Cassidy,' I says."

Government by Whipping Postmaster

"I see," said Mr. Dooley, "that th' Prisidint is plannin' an attack on th' good old English custom iv

wife-beatin'. He wants to inthrajooce th' other good
old English instichoochion iv a whippin'-post."

"He's all right," said Mr. Hennessy. "I'd like to
have th' job."

"So wud I," said Mr. Dooley. "If th' law iver goes
through I'll run f'r sheriff an' promise to give back
all me salary an' half what I get fr'm th' race-
thracks. Not, mind ye, that wife-beatin' is much
practised in this counthry. Slug-ye'er-spouse is an
internaytional spoort that has niver become pop'lar
on our side iv th' wather. An American lady is not
th' person that anny man but a thrained athlete wud
care to raise his hand again' save be way iv smooth-
in' her hair. Afther goin' to a school an' larnin' to
box, throw th' shot, an' play right-guard on th' fut-
ball team th' gentle crather has what Hogan calls
an abundant stock iv repartee. In me life I've known
on'y six haitchool wife-beaters. Two iv thim were
lucky to beat their wives to th' sidewalk, an' I've res-
cued th' other four fr'm th' roof iv th' house with a
ladder. But now an' thin I suppose an American gintleman, afther losin' three or four fights on his way
home, does thry to make a repytation be swingin'
on th' ex-heavy-weight champeen iv th' Siminary f'r
Rayfined Females, an' if she can't put th' baby on
th' flure in time to get to wurruk with th' loose parts
iv th' stove, 'tis Thaydore's idee that she shud call
a polisman an' have father taken down to th' jail an'
heartily slapped.

"An' he's right. No gintleman shud wallop his
wife, an' no gintleman wud. I'm in favor iv havin'

wife-beaters whipped, an' I'll go further an' say that 'twud be a good thing to have ivry marrid man scoorged about wanst a month. As a bachelor man, who rules entirely be love, I've spint fifty years invistigatin' what Hogan calls th' martial state, an' I've come to th' con-clusion that ivry man uses vilence to his wife. He may not beat her with a table-leg, but he coerces her with his mind. He can put a savage remark to th' pint iv th' jaw with more lastin' effect thin a right hook. He may not dhrag her around be th' hair iv her head, but he dhrags her be her sympathies, her fears, an' her anxieties. As a last raycoorse he beats her be doin' things that make her pity him. An' th' ladies, Gawd bless thim, like it. Th' whippin'-post f'r wife-beaters won't be popylar with th' wife-beaters. In her heart ivry woman likes th' sthrong arm. Ye very sildom see th' wife iv an habitchool wife-beater lavin' him. Th' husband that gives his wife a vilet bokay is as apt to lose her as th' husband that gives her a vilet eye. Th' man that breaks th' furniture, tips over th' table, kicks th' dog, an' pegs th' lamp at th' lady iv his choice is seen no more often in our justly popylar divoorce coorts thin th' man who comes home arly to feed th' canary. Manny a skilful mandolin player has been onable to prevint his wife fr'm elopin' with a prize-fighter.

"No, you won't find anny malthreated ladies' names on th' petition f'r th' new govermint depart-mint. Th' Whippin' Postmasther-Gin'ral will have to look elsewhere f'r applause thin to th' down-throdden wives iv th' counthry. But th' departmint has come to stay; I hope, Hinnissy, to see its mission enlarged. I look forward to th' day whin there will be a govermint whippin'-post, with a large American flag at th' top iv it, in ivry American city. Afther a while we can attind to th' wants iv th' rural communities. A fourth assistant whippin' postmasther-gin'ral will be sint to th' farmin' counthry, so that Cy an' Alick will get just as good a lammin' as Alphonso an' Augustus. He will carry a red, white an' blue post on his thravels, an' a special cat-o'-nine-tails, with th' arms iv th' United States an' th' motto, 'Love wan another,' engraved on th' handle. Th' whippin'-post will grow up to be wan iv th' foundations iv our govermint, like th' tariff. Whin annybody proposes to abolish it they will be met with th' cry: 'Let th' whippin'-post be rayformed be its frinds.' Th' frinds will build a bigger post an' put a few nails on th' lash. Ivinchooly people will quit goin' to Mr. Vernon an' make pilgrimages to Delaware, where th' whippin'-post has had such a fine moral effect. An' thin Addicks will be ilicted prisidint.

"Won't it be fine? Th' govermint gives us too little amusemint nowadays. Th' fav'rite pastime iv civilized man is croolty to other civilized man. Ye take a Southern gintleman, who has been accustomed to pathronize th' lynchin' iv naygurs. All other spoorts seem tame to him aftherward. He won't go to th' theaytre or th' circus, but pines at home till there's another black man to be burned. A

warden iv a pinitinchry niver has anny fun out iv
life afther he loses his job.   Judges in civil coorts
sometimes resign, but niver a hangin' judge in a
criminal coort.

"Yes, sir, 'twill be a good thing f'r th' criminal an'
a good thing f'r a spoort-lovin' public, but th' question that comes up in me mind is, Will it be a good
thing f'r Uncle Sam an' a good thing f'r Sheriff
Dooley. Th' only habit a man or a govermint ought
to pray again' acquirin' is croolty. It's th' gr-reatest
dissypation in th' wurruld. Ye can't swear off bein'
crool wanst ye begin to make a practice iv it.   Ye
keep gettin' crooler an' crooler, till ye fin'lly think iv
nawthin' but injurin' ye'er neighbor an' seein' him
suffer. I mind wanst, whin I was a boy at home, a
new schoolmasther come to th' hedge. He was a nice,
quiet, near-sighted young fellow, an' he began be
larrupin' on'y th' worst iv th' boys. But ye cud see
in a minyit that he was injyin' th' pastime. At th'
end iv th' month he was lickin' somebody all th' time.
He used to get fairly dhrunk switchin' us. Glory be,
it seems to me that I spint all me boyhood days on
another boy's shoulders. He licked us f'r ivrything,
an' annythin' an' nawthin' at all.   It wasn't that it
done us anny good, but it gave him pleasure. He's
been dead an' gone these forty years, an' I bear him
no ill-will, but if I iver r-run acrost his ghost I'll put
a head on it.

"So it is with Uncle Sam: If he begins to lick wife-
beaters, befure he's been at it long he won't have
anny time f'r annythin' but th' whippin'-post. He'll

be in his shirt-sleeves all day long, slashin' away at countherfeiters, illicit distillers, postal thieves, an' dimmycrats.

"No, Hinnissy, there ain't a hair's diff'rence between a blackguard who beats his wife an' a govermint that beats its childher. Ye can't cure corp'ral punishmint be makin' th' govermint th' biggest kind iv corp'ral punisher. Ye can't inflict corp'ral punishmint onless ye'er sthronger thin' th' fellow ye punish, an' if ye ar-re sthronger ye ought to be ashamed iv ye'ersilf. Whiniver I hear iv a big six-fut schoolteacher demandin' that he be allowed to whale a thirty-two-inch child I feel like askin' him up here to put on th' gloves with Jeffreys. Whin a govermint or a man raysorts to blows it shows they're ayether afraid or have lost their timpers. An' there ye ar-re."

"Spare th' rod an' spile th' child." said Mr. Hennessy.

"Yes," said Mr. Dooley, "but don' spare th' rod an' ye spile th' rod, th' child, an' th' child's father."

On Tinkering with the Capitalist System

Saturday night at Mr. Dooley's—Mr Dooley in the chair. Present, Mr. Larkin and Mr. McKenna. Present, but not voting, Mr. Hennessy and Mr. Schwartzmeister.

"Socialism is sweepin' like a wave over th' counthry," said Mr. Larkin, the radical blacksmith.

"It hasn't wet my feet yet," said Mr. McKenna (Rep.).

"But Matthew is right," said Mr. Dooley. "He's right about it. A few days ago Mulligan wud've r-run me in because I didn't wear a pitcher iv Hetty Green in me watch-chain, an' sind me freeman's sufferage to Pierpont Mulligan to be endorsed befure I cud use it. Today Mulligan is prisidint iv th' Polisman's Binivolent Hammer th' Millyonaires Association, an' he has turned to th' wall th' lithygrafts iv th' fathers iv his counthry, Addicks Crossin' th' Delaware, Jakey Schiff sthrikin' th' shekels fr'm th' slave, an' Grover Cleveland's Farewell to his Life-insurance agents. These an' other gr-reat names that wanst us bold but busted peasanthry looked up to f'r advice that not on'y cost thim nawthin', but was even what ye might call remoonerative to thim, has to pay th' same rates as Mrs. Winslow's soothin' syrup to have their pathriotic appeals to their fellow-citizens printed in the pa-apers. As Hogan wud say, ye can no longer conjure with thim. Ye can't even con with them, as I wud say.

"It was diff'rent in the goolden days. A gr-reat chance a Socialist had thin. If annybody undherstood him he was kilt be infuryated wurrukinmen. It was a good thing f'r him that he on'y spoke German, which is a language not gin'rally known among cultivated people, Schwartzmeister. They used to hold their meetin's in a cellar in Wintworth Avnoo, an' th' meetin' was most always followed be an outin' in th' pathrol-wagon. 'Twas wan iv th' spoorts to go down to see th' Brotherhood iv Man rushed off in th' on'y Municipal Ownership conveyance we

had in thim days, an' havin' their spectacles busted
be th' hardy an' loyal polis.

" 'Tis far diff'rent now. No cellars f'r th' Brotherhood iv Man, but Mrs. Vanderhankerbilk give a
musical soree f'r th' ladies iv th' Female Billyonairs
Arbeiter Verein at her iligant Fifth Avnoo mansion
yisterday afthernoon. Th' futmen were dhressed in
th' costume iv th' Fr-rinch Rivolution, an' tea was
served in imitation bombs. Th' meetin' was ad-
dhressed be th' well-known Socialist leader, J. Clar-
ence Lumley, heir to th' Lumley millyons. This well-
known prolytariat said he had become a Socialist
through studyin' his father. He cud not believe that
a system was right which allowed such a man to accumylate three hundherd millyon dollars. He had
frequently thried to inthrest this vin'rable mossback
in industhreel questions, an' all he replied was: 'Get
th' money.' Th' ladies prisint cud appreciate how
foolish th' captains iv industhree are, because they
were marrid to thim an' knew what they looked like
in th' mornin'. Th' time had come whin a fierce blow
must be sthruck f'r human freedom. In conclusion,
he wud sing th' 'Marsellaisy,' an' accompany himsilf
on a guitar. Th' hostess followed with a few remarks. She said Socialists were not dhreamers, but
practical men. Socialism was not a question iv th'
hour, but had come to stay as an afthernoon intertainmint. It was less expinsive thin bridge, an' no
wan cud call ye down f'r ladin' out iv th wrong hand.
She had made up her mind that ivrybody must do
something f'r th' cause. It was wrong f'r her to have

other people wurrukin' f'r her, an' she intinded to
free or bounce her servants an' go to live at a hotel.
She wud do her share in th' wurruld's wurruk, too,
an' with this in view she was takin' lessons in mini-
chure paintin'. A lady prisint asked Mr. Lumley wud
large hats be worn undher Socialism. He answered
no, but th' more becomin' toque; but he wud look
th' matther up in a book be Karl Marx that he undherstood was an authority on these subjects. Th'
meetin' thin adjourned afther passin' a resolution
callin' on th' husband iv th' hostess to go an jump in
th' river.

"An' there ye ar-re, boys. Socialism is no longer
talked to ye in Platt Doitch, but handed to ye fr'm
th' top iv a coach or whispered fr'm behind an ivory
fan. It's betther that way. I prefer to have it in a
goblet all iv goold fr'm fair hands to takin' it out iv
a can. Ye can't make anny new idee too soft f'r me.
If I had me way I'd get thim to put it to music an'
have it danced befure me. It suits me betther th'
way it is thin whin Schulz screened a Schwabian account iv it through his whiskers. 'What d'ye want to
do?' says I. 'To make all men akel,' says he. 'Akel to
who?' says I. 'If ye mane akel to me, I'm agreeable,'
I says. 'I tire iv bein' supeeryor to th' rest iv th'
race,' says I. 'But,' says I, 'if ye mane akel to ye,'
says I, 'I'll throuble ye to take ye'rsilf off,' says I. 'I
shave,' says I."

"But suppose you did get Socialism. What would
you do?" asked Mr. McKenna (Rep.).

"Bebel says—" began Mr. Schwartzmeister.

"Shut up, Schwartz," said Mr. Larkin. "Th' first thing we'd do wud be to take all th' money in th' wurruld an' throw it into th' lake."

"Not my money," said Mr. McKenna.

"Yes, ye'er's an' ivrybody else's, said Mr. Larkin.

"Mine wudden't make much iv a splash," said Mr. Hennessy.

"Hush," said Mr. Larkin. "Thin we'd set ivry wan to wurruk at something."

"What wurruk wud ye put us at?" asked Mr. McKenna.

"Liebnicht says—" began Mr. Schwartzmeister.

"Niver mind what he says," said Mr. Larkin. "Ivry man wud wurruk at what plazed him."

"But suppose no wurruk plazed him," said Mr. Dooley and Mr. McKenna at once.

"He'd starve," said Mr. Larkin.

"He wud," said Mr. Dooley.

"Well," said Mr. McKenna, after some thought, "I choose to feed th' swans in Lincoln Park."

"Ye cudden't," said Mr. Larkin. "Ye wudden't be let. Whin ye'er case come up I'd be called in as an expert an' I'd sind th' good woman over to th' governmint hat-store f'r th' loan iv a stove-pipe, jump on a govermint sthreet-car r-run be me cousin, an' go down to th' City Hall or govermint Intillijence Office. Afther shakin' me warmly be th' hand an' givin' me a govermint stogy to smoke, th' Mayor wud say: 'Little Jawnny McKenna is a candydate f'r feedin' th' swans in Lincoln Park. He has O'Brien

an' a sthrong dillygation behind him, but what I
want to know is, is he fitted f'r th' job?' 'I'm afraid
not,' says I. 'He hasn't got th' requisite touch. But
if ye want an expert hand f'r th' wheelbarrow at
th' govermint rollin'-mills, he's jus' th' good,
sthrong, poor fellow f'r th' sinycure,' says I. An' th'
nex' day at siven o'clock they'd be a polisman at th'
dure an' ye'd be put in handcuffs an' dhragged off to
th' slag pile. An' maybe I wudden't break ye'er back.
F'r I'd be ye'er boss. I'm wan iv th' original old-line
Socialists, an' to th' victor belongs th' spoils, be
Hivens."

"You'd not be my boss then any more than you
are now, me boy," said Mr. McKenna, warmly.

"In Chermany—" began Mr. Schwartzmeister.

"Dhry up," said Mr. Larkin. "Ye mustn't feel
badly, Jawn. Ye wudden't have to wurruk long.
About eight o'clock Martin's shift wud come on,
ye'd make a date to meet me at th' govermint baseball game, take off ye'er overalls, jump into ye'er
autymobill, an' dash over to what used to be Martin's place, but is now a govermint dispinsary, where
an uncle iv mine wud give ye a much larger glass iv
malt free, d'ye mind."

"Hooray!" said Mr. Hennessy.

"Thin ye'd run over to ye'er iligant brown-
stone mansion in Mitchigan Avnoo, beautifully fur-
nished be th' govermint; a govermint dhressmaker
wud be thryin' a new dhress on ye'er wife, a letther-
carrier wud be milkin' a govermint cow on th' back
lawn, an' all ye'd have to do f'r th' rest iv th' day

wud be to smoke ye'er pipe an' play on th' accorjeen."

"It sounds good," said Mr. McKenna. "But—"

"In Karl Marx—" began Mr. Schwartzmeister.

"Keep quite," said Mr. Dooley. "Ye mustn't mon-
nopolize th' convarsation, Schwartz. It's gettin' to
be a habit with ye. I must tell ye f'r ye'er own good.
Give somebody else a chance wanst in a while. What
were ye goin' to say, Jawn?"

"I wasn't goin' to say annything," said Mr. Mc-
Kenna. "What's the use arguing against a balloon
ascension? The grand old Republican party, under
such leaders as—"

"Ye needn't mintion thim," said Mr. Dooley, "until this month's grand jury has adjourned. But ye'er
right. Th' grand ol' Raypublican party will take
care iv this matther. A Raypublican is born ivry
minyit, an' they will niver allow money bearin' th'
sacred image iv Columbya to be dhrowned in th'
lake. It's no use argyin' again' Socialism, an' be th'
same token, it's no use argyin' f'r it. Afther listenin' to Larkin an' his talkative German frind here, I
don't know anny more about it thin I did befure. Schwartzmeister's idee iv it is that ivry man
shall live in a story-an'-a-half house, wear a unyform with a cock's feather in th' hat, an' dhraw his
pay in soup tickets fr'm th' German govermint.
Larkin is lookin' forward to a chance to get even
with his boss. That's his idee iv an industhreel
Hiven. Th' Lord knows I'd rejoice to see th' day
whin Hinnissy wud be shakin' a throwel fr'm th'

top iv a wall an' yellin' 'Mort' at Andhrew Carnaygie scramblin' bare-legged up a ladder, or mesilf lyin' back on a lounge afther a hard day's wurruk
writin' pothry f'r th' govermint, ordherin' th' King
iv England to bring me a poached egg an' a cup iv
tay, an' be quick about it, darn ye.

"But I'm afraid it won't happen in our day. That
alone wud make me a Socialist. I'm sthrong f'r anny
rivolution that ain't goin' to happen in me day. But
th' thruth is, me boy, that nawthin' happens, annyhow. I see gr-reat changes takin' place ivry day, but
no change at all ivry fifty years. What we call this
here counthry iv ours pretinds to want to thry new
experiments, but a sudden change gives it a chill.
It's been to th' circus an' bought railroad tickets in
a hurry so often that it thinks quick change is short
change. Whin I take me mornin' walk an' see little
boys an' girls with their dinnerpails on their arms
goin' down to th' yards I'm th' hottest Socialist ye
iver see. I'd be annything to stop it. I'd be a Raypublican, even. But whin I think how long this foolish old buildin' has stood, an' how manny a good
head has busted again' it, I begin to wondher
whether 'tis anny use f'r ye or me to thry to bump
it off th' map. Larkin here says th' capitalist system is made up iv th' bones iv billions iv people, like
wan iv thim coral reefs that I used to think was pe-
thrified sponge. If that is so, maybe th' on'y thing I
can do about it is to plant a few geeranyums, injye
thim while I live, an' thin conthribute me own busted
shoulder-blades f'r another Rockyfellar to walk on."

On the New York Custom House

"Hannigan's back," said Mr. Dooley.

"I didn't know he'd iver been away," said Mr. Hennessy.

"O, he has that," said Mr. Dooley. "He's been makin' what Hogan calls th' gran' tower. He's been to New York an' to Cork, an' he see his rilitives, an' now he's come home f'r to thry to get even. He had a gran' time, an' some day I'll get him in here an' have him tell ye about it."

"Did he bring annything back?" asked Mr. Hennessy.

"He started to," said Mr. Dooley. "Befure he left Queenstown he laid in a supply iv th' stimulant that's made th' Irish th' finest potes an' rivolutionists, an' th' poorest bookkeepers in th' wurruld, an' a dozen or two iv blackthorn sticks f'r frinds iv his on th' polis. He had a most tumulchuse v'yage. There was a man played th' accorjeen all th' way acrost. Glad he was to see th' pleasant fields iv Noo Jarsey an' th' sthreet clanin' department's scows goin' out to sea, an' th' la-ad fr'm th' health boord comin' aboord an' askin' ivrybody did they have th' smallpox an' was they convicts. There was a Rooshian aboord that'd been run out iv Rooshia because he cud r-read, an' people thought he gettin' ready to peg something at th' czar an' Hannigan an' him got to be gr-reat frinds. As they sthud on th' deck, Hannigan banged him on th' back an,' says he: 'Look,' he says, with th' tears r-runnin' down his cheeks. He was wanst in th' legislachure. 'Look,' he says, 'ye poor down-throdden serf,' he says. 'Behold, th' land iv freedom,' he says, 'where ivry man's as good as ivry other man,' he says, 'on'y th' other man don't know it.' he says. 'That flag which I can't see, but I know 'tis there,' he says, 'floats over no race iv slaves,' he says. 'Whin I shtep off th' boat,' he says, 'I'll put me box on me shouldher,' he says, 'an' I'll be as free as anny man alive,' he says, 'an' if e'er a sowl speaks to me, I'll give him a dhrink out iv th' bottle or a belt with th' blackthorn,' he says, 'an' little I care which it is,' he says. "A smile f'r those that love ye, an' a punch f'r those that hate, as Tom Moore, th' pote, says,' he says. 'Land iv liberty,' he says, 'I salute ye,' he says, wavin' his hat at a soap facthry. 'Have ye declared yet? says a man at his elbow. 'Declared what?' says Hannigan. 'Th' things ye have in th' box,' says th' man. 'I have not,' says Hannigan. 'Th' contints iv that crate is sacred between me an mesilf,' he says. 'Well,' says th' man, 'ye'd betther slide down th' companyion way or stairs to th' basemint iv th' ship an' tell what ye know,' he says, 'or 'tis mindin' bar'ls at th' pinitinchry ye'll be this day week,' he says.

"Well, Hannigan is an Irish raypublican that does what he's told, so he wint down stairs an' there was a lot iv la-ads settin' ar-round a table, an' says wan iv thim: What's ye'er name, Tim Hannigan, an' ar-re ye a citizen iv this countrhy?' 'Well, glory be to th' saints!' says Hannigan, 'if that ain't Petie Casey, th' tailor' son. Well, how ar-re ye an' what ar-re ye doin' down here?' he says. 'I'm a customs

D—8

inspictor,' says th' boy. ' 'Tis a good job,' says Hannigan, 'I thried f'r it wanst mesilf but I jined th' wrong or-gan-ization,' he says. 'Step out an' have a dhrink,' he says. 'I've a bottle iv Irish whisky in my thrunk that'd make ye think ye was swallowin' a pincushion,' he says. 'Sh-h,' says Petie Casey. 'Man alive, ye'll be in th' lock-up in another minyit if ye don't keep quite. That fellow behind ye is a mannyfacthrer iv Irish Whisky in Bleecker sthreet an' he's hand in glove with Mack,' he says. 'Well, annyhow,' says Hannigan, 'I want to give ye a blackthorn sthick f'r ye'er father,' he says. 'Lord bless me sowl!' says th' boy. 'Ye'll lose me me job yet. That fellow with th' r-red hair is th' principal Rahway dealer in blackthorns. His name is Schmidt, an' Mack sinds him down here f'r to see that th' infant industhryies iv Rahway don't git th' worst iv it fr'm th' pauper labor iv Europe,' he says. With that, th' chief inspictor come up an' says he: 'Misther Hannigan' he says, 'on ye'er wurrud iv honor as an Irish gintleman an' an American citizen,' he says, 'have ye annthing in that box that ye cud've paid more f'r in this counthry?' 'On me wurrud iv honor,' says Hannigan. 'I believe ye,' says th' chief. 'Swear him. Ye know th' solemnity iv an oath. Ye do solemnly swear be this an' be that that ye have not been lyin' all this time like th' knavish scoundrel that ye wud be if ye did,' he says. 'I swear,' says Hannigan. 'That will suffice,' says th' chief. 'Ye look like an honest man, an' if ye've perjured ye'ersilf ye'll go to jail,' he says. 'Ye're an American citizen an' ye

wudden't lie,' he says. 'We believe ye an' Mack believes an' th' sicrety iv th' threeasury believes ye as
much as they wud thimsilves,' he says. 'Go down on
th' dock an' be searched.'

"Hannigan says he wint down on th' dock practisin' th' lock step, so he wudden't seem green whin
they put him in f'r perjury. I won't tell ye what he
see on th' dock. No, I won't, Hinnissy. 'Tisn't annything ye ought to know, onless ye're goin' into th'
dhry goods business. Hannigan says they hadn't
got half way to th' bottom iv th' thrunks an' there
wasn't a woman fr'm th' boat that he'd dare to look
in th' face. He tur-rned away with a blush an' see
his wife an' childher standin' behind th' bars iv a
fence an' he started f'r thim. 'Hol' on there,' says a
polisman, 'Where are ye goin'?' he says. 'To see me
wife, ye gom,' says Hannigan. 'Ye can't see her till
we look at what ye've got in th' box,' says th' copper. 'Ye'er domestic jooties can wait ontil we see
about th' others,' says he. 'Yere a prisoner,' says he,
'till we prove that ye ought to be,' he says. With
that Mrs. Hannigan calls out: 'Tim,' she says, 'Pah-
pah,' she says. 'Ar-re ye undher arrest?' she says.
'An' ye promised me ye wudden't dhrink,' she says.
'What ar-re ye charged with?' she says. 'Threason,'
says he. 'I wint away fr'm home,' he says. 'But
that's no crime,' she says. 'Yes it is,' says he. 'I come
back,' he says.

"With that another inspictor come along an' he
says: 'Open that thrunk,' he says. 'Cut th' rope,' he
says. 'Boys, bring an axe an' lave us see what this

smuggler has in th' box,' he says. 'What's this? A blackthorn cane! Confiscate it. A bottle iv whisky. Put it aside f'r ividence. A coat! Miscreent! A pair iv pants! Ye perjured ruffyan! Don't ye know ye can get nearly as good pair iv pants f'r twice th' money in this counthry? Three collars? Hyena! A bar iv soap. An' this man calls himself a pathriot! Where did ye get that thrunk? It looks foreign. I'll take it. Open ye'er mouth. I'll throuble ye f'r that back tooth. Me man,' he says, 'ye have taken a long chance,' he says, 'but I won't be hard on ye. Ye'll need clothes,' he says. 'Here's me card,' he says. 'I'm an inspictor iv customs on th' side, but th' govermint really hires me to riprisint Guldenheim an' Eckstein, shirt makers, be appintmint to th' cabinet, an' Higgins an' Co., authors iv th' Non-Combustible Canton (o.) Pant. A good pant. If ye want annything in our line, call on our store. No throuble to take money.'

"Hannigan wint out an' found Honorya an' th' childher had gone off f'r to get a bondsman. Thin he tur-rned an' called out to th' inspictor: 'Look here, you!' 'What is it?' says th' man. 'Ye missed something,' says Hannigan. 'I was tattooed in Cork,' he says. 'Stop that man,' says th' head iv a ladin' firm iv tattooers an prisidint iv th' society f'r th' Protection iv American Art, If Such There Be. 'Stop him, he's smugglin' in foreign art!' he says. But Hannigan bate him to th' sthreet car. An' that was his welcome home.

" 'Call me Hanniganoffski,' says he las' night. 'I'm

goin' to Rooshia,' he says. 'F'r to be a slave iv th' Czar?' says I. 'Well,' says he, 'if I've got to be a slave,' he says, 'I'd rather be opprissed be th' Czar thin by a dealer in shirt waists,' he says. 'Th' Czar ain't so bad,' he says. 'He don't care what I wear undherneath,' he says.

"Oh, well, divvle mend Hannigan," said Mr. Hennessy. "It's little sympathy I have f'r him, gallivantin' off acrost th' ocean an' spindin' money he earned at home. Anyhow, Hannigan an' th' likes iv him is all raypublicans."

"That's why I can't make it out," said Mr. Dooley. "Why do they stick him up? Maybe th' sicrety iv th' threeasury is goin' in to what Hogan calls th' lingery business an' is gettin' information on th' fashions. But I wondher why they make him swear to affidavits."

" 'Tis wrong," said Mr. Hennessy, "We're an honest people."

"We are," said Mr. Dooley. "We are, but we don' know it."

INTERNATIONAL LAW

On the Hague Conference

"I see," said Mr. Hennessy, "we're goin' to sind th' navy to th' Passyfic."

"I see we're not, too," said Mr. Dooley. "There's two sides to iv'ry question, an' in Washington there are twinty-two to iv'ry answer. Wan day sees th' navy tearin' around th' Horn, not to intimydate th' Japs, mind ye, but on'y to show thim that if they're lookin' f'r throuble they can have it without movin' out iv their back yards. Another day th' navy is still at home explodin' itsilf. Th' navy gun, her name was Maude. I wudden't want to be in front iv wan iv thim gr-reat injines iv destruction, but if I had to make me choice an' all th' places undherneath were taken, I'd rather be in front thin behind. F'r purposes iv safety they ought to be pointed th' other way. If war comes th' minyit we turn our guns on th' inimy 'twill be all over with him.

"No sir, I can't tell whether th' navy is goin' to spend th' rest iv its days protectin' what Hogan calls our insulted possessions in th' Oryent or whether it is to remain in th' neighborhood iv Barnstable makin' th' glaziers iv New England rich beyond th' dhreams iv New England avarice, which ar're hopeful dhreams. Th' cabinet is divided, th' sicrety iv th' navy is divided, th' Prisidint is divided an' th' press is divided. Wan great iditor, fr'm his post iv danger in Paris, has ordhered th' navy to report at San Francisco at four eight next Thursday. Another great iditor livin' in Germany has warned it that it will do so at its peril. Nawthin' is so fine as to see a great modhern journalist unbend fr'm his mighty task iv selectin' fr'm a bunch iv phottygrafts th' prettiest cook iv Flatbush or engineerin' with his great furrowed brain th' Topsy Fizzle compytition to trifle with some light warm-weather subject like internaytional law or war. But men such as these can do annything.

"But, annyhow, what diff'rence does it make whether th' navy goes to th' Passyfic or not? If it goes at all it won't be to make war. They've dumped all th' fourteen-inch shells into th' sea. Th' ammunition hoists ar-re filled with american beauty roses an' orchids. The guns are loaded with confetty. Th' officers dhrink nawthin' sthronger thin vanilla an' sthrawberry mixed. Whin th' tars go ashore they hurry at wanst to th' home iv th' Christyan Indeavor Society or throng th' free libries readin' religious pothry. Me frind Bob Evens is goin' to contribute a series iv articles to th' Ladies' Home Journal on croshaying. F'r th' Hague Peace Conference has abolished war, Hinnissy. Ye've seen the last war ye'll iver see, me boy.

"Th' Hague conference, Hinnissy, was got up be th' Czar iv Rooshya just befure he moved his army agin th' Japs. It was a quiet day at Saint Pethersburg. Th' prime minister had just been blown up with dinnymite, th' Czar's uncle had been shot an' wan iv his cousins was expirin' fr'm a dose iv proosic acid. All was comparitive peace in th' warrum summer's afternoon th' Czar felt almost dhrousy as he set in his rile palace an' listened to th' low, monotonous drone iv bombs beein' hurled at th' Probojensky guards, an' picked th' broken glass out iv th' dhrink that'd just been brought to him be an aged servitor who was prisidint iv th' Saint Pethersburg lodge iv Pathriotic Assassins. Th' monarch's mind turned to th' subjick iv war, an' he says to himself: 'What a dhreadful thing it is that such a beautiful wurruld shud be marred be thousands iv innicint men bein' sint out to shoot each other f'r no cause whin they might betther stay at home an' wurruk f'r their rile masters,' he says. 'I will disguise mesilf as a moojik an' go over to th' tillygraft office an' summon a meetin' iv th' powers,' he says.

"That's how it come about. All th' powers sint dillgates an' a gr-reat manny iv th' weaknesses did so too. They met last week in Holland an' they have been devotin' all their time since to makin' war impossible in th' future. Th' meetin' was opened with an acrimonyous debate over a resolution offered be a dillygate fr'm Paryguay callin' f'r immejit disarmamint, which is th' same, Hinnissy, as notifyin' th' Powers to turn in their guns to th' man at th' dure. This was carried be a very heavy majority. Among those that voted in favor iv it were: Paryguay, Uryguay, Switzerland, Chiny, Belgium an' San Marino. Opposed were England, France, Rooshya, Germany, Italy, Austhree, Japan an' th' United States.

"Th' Hon'rable Joe Choate, dillygate fr'm th'

United States moved that in future wars enlisted man shud not wear ear-rings. Carried, on'y Italy votin' no.

"Th' conference thin discussed blowin' up th' enimy with dinnymite, poisinin' him, shootin' th' wounded, settin' fire to infants, bilin' prisoners-iv-war in hot lard an' robbin' graves. Some excitement was created durin' th' talk be th' dillygate fr'm th' cannybal islands, who proposed that prisoners-iv-war be eaten. Th' German dillygate thought that this was carryin' a specyal gift iv wan power too far. It wud give th' cannybal islands a distinct advantage in case iv war, as Europeen sojers were accustomed to horses. Th' English dilligate said that while much cud be said against a practice which personally seemed to him rather unsportsmanlike, still he felt he must reserve th' right iv anny cannybal allies iv Brittanya to go as far as they liked.

"Th' Hon'rable Joe Choate moved that in future wars no military band shud be considered complete without a base-dhrum. Carried.

"Th' entire South American dillygation said that no nation ought to go to war because another nation wanted to hang it up on th' slate. Th' English dillygate was much incensed. 'Why gintlemen,' says he, 'if ye deprived us iv th' right to collect debts be killin' th' debtor ye wud take away fr'm war its entire moral purpose. I must ask ye again to cease thinkin' on this subject in a gross, mateeryal way an' considher th' moral side alone,' he says. Th' conference was much moved be this pathetic speech, th' dillygate fr'm France wept softly into his hanker-chef an' th' dillygate fr'm Germany wint over an' forcibly took an open-face goold watch fr'm th' dillygate fr'm Vinzwala.

"Th' Hon'rable Joe Choate moved that all future wars horses shud be fed with hay wheriver possible. Carried.

"A long informal talk on th' reinthroduction iv scalpin' followed. At last th' dillygate fr'm Chiny arose an' says he: 'I'd like to know what war is. What is war annyhow?' 'Th' Lord knows, we don't,' says th' chairman. 'We're all profissors iv colledges or lawyers whin we're home,' he says. 'Is it war to shoot my aunt?' says he. 'Robbery is a nicissary part iv war,' says th' English dillygate, 'F'r th' pur-pose iv enfoorcin' a moral example,' he says. 'Well,' says old Wow Chow, 'I'd like to be able to go back home an' tell thim what war really is. A few years back ye sint a lot iv young men over to our part iv th' wurruld an' without sayin' with ye'er leave or by ye'er leave they shot us an' they hung us up be our psyche knots an' they burned down our little bam-boo houses. Thin they wint up to Pekin, set fire to th' town an' stole ivrything in sight. I just got out iv th' back dure in time to escape a jab in th' spine fr'm a German that I niver see befure. If it hadn't been that whin I was a boy I won th' hundred yards at th' university iv Slambang in two hours an' forty minyits, an' if it hadn't happened that I was lightly dhressed in a summer overskirt an' a thin blouse an' if th' German hadn't stopped to steal me garters,

I wudden't be here at this moment,' says he. 'Was that war, or wan't it?' he says. 'It was an expedition,' says th' dillygate fr'm England, 'to serve th' high moral jooties iv Christyan civvylization.' 'Thin,' says th' dillygate fr'm Chiny, puttin' on his hat, 'I'm f'r war,' he says. 'It aint so rough,' he says. An' he wint home."

"But is th' navy goin' to th' Passyfic?" asked Mr. Hennessy.

"If ye took a vote in th' navy on it ye bet it wud" said Mr. Dooley. "That's th' throuble about these here movements f'r peace. We use th' wrong kind iv people to stop war. Instead iv usin' pro-fissors an' lawyers we ought to use sojars. A peace movement that cud get th' support iv th' United States navy wud be worth while. Let ivry man do what he can in his own way. Let him attend to th' thing he knows most about. Let th' sojers stop war an' th' pro-fissors stop talking."

Mr. Dooley Calls For An International Police Force

"I thought," said Mr. Dooley, "that whin me young frind th' czar iv Rooshya got up that there Dutch polis coort f'r to settle th' back-yard quar'ls among th' nations iv th' arth, 'twud be th' end iv war f'r good an' all. It looked all right to me. Why not? If be anny chanst I get mesilf full iv misconduck an' go ar-round thryin' to collect me debts with a gun, an' camp out in somebody's house an' won't lave, th' polis take me down to Deerin' sthreet station an' throw me in among th' little playmates

iv th' criminal, an' in th' mornin' I'm befure me
cousin, th' chief justice, an' he con-fiscates th' guns
an' sinds me up th' bullyvard f'r thirty days. Why
not th' same thing f'r th' powers, whin they go off
on a tear? I thought I'd be readin' in th pa-apers:
'Judge Oolenboff at th' Hague coort had a large
docket yisterdah mornin'. Thirty mimbers iv th' notoryous Hapsburg fam'ly was sint up f'r varyous
terms, an' th' polis think they have completely broke
up th' gang. Th' king iv Spain was charged with
nonsupport, but was dismissed with a warnin'. Th'
impror iv Chiny was let off with a fine f'r maintainin' a dope jint, an' warrants was issued f'r th' owners iv th' primises, th' king iv England an' th' czar
of Rooshya. Th' Sultan iv Turkey, alias Hamid th'
Hick, alias th' Turrible Turk, was charged with
polygamy. Th' coort give him th' alternative iv five
more wives or thirty days. Whin these cases had
been cleared away, th' bailiff led into th' dock three
notoryous charackters. Th' first was a large, heavy-
set German, who proved to be Bill th' Bite, less
known by his thrue name iv Willim H.J.E.I.K.L.M.-
N.O.P.Q.R.S.T., etc., Hohenzollern. By his side was
an undersized little man, th' notoryous Casthro, a
pro-fissyonal dead beat an' imbizzler, an' a stout
party be th' name iv Albert Edward, or Edwards,
who is said be th' internaytional polis to be behind
some iv th' biggest grafts that have been run
through f'r th' las' twenty years, though niver so far
caught with th' goods on. Hohenzollern was accused
iv assault with intint to kill, robbery, blackmail,

carryin' concealed weepins an' raysistin' an officer. Edward or Edwards was charged with maintainin' a fence f'r rayceivin' stolen property an' carryin' concealed weepins. Casthro was charged with vagrancy, maintainin' a disordherly house an' fraud.

" 'Th' attorney f'r th' pro-secution made out a sthrong case again' th' pris'ners. He said that Hohenzollern was a desprit character, who was constantly a menace to th' peace iv th' wurruld. He had no sympathy f'r Casthro, who was an idle, dangerous ruffyan, an' he hoped th' coort wud dale severely with him. He niver paid his debts, an' none iv th' neighbors chickens was safe fr'm him. He was a low-down, worthless, mischief-makin' loafer. But Casthro's bad charackter did not excuse th' other pris'ners. It seems that Casthro, who niver paid annybody annything, owed a bill with th' well-known grocery firm iv Schwartzheim an' Hicks, which he rayfused to settle. Hearin' iv this, Hohenzollern an' Edward or Edwards con-spired together to go to Casthro's place undher pretinse iv collectin' th' bill an' throw Casthro out an' take possission iv his property. Hohenzollern was th' more vilent iv th' pair. He appeared carryin' loaded revolvers, which he fired into th' windows iv Casthro's shop, smashed in th' dure an' endangered th' lives iv manny innocint people. He was ar-rested afther a sthruggle, in which he severely injured wan iv th' internaytional polis foorce, an' was carried off in a hurry-up wagon. Edward or Edwards was caught in th' neighborhood. He pretinded to be an innocint spectator, but whin sarched was found to have loaded revolvers in his pocket, as well as an addhress to th' Christian nations iv th' wurruld, justifyin' his conduck an' denouncin' his accomplice. Casthro was taken into custody on gin-ral principles. Th' prosecution asked that an example be made iv th' pris'ners. Afther tistymony had been inthrojooced showin' th' bad charackter iv th' men in th' dock, Hohenzollern was put on th' stand to testify to his own definse. He swore that he had no inmity again' Casthro, but Schwarztheim iv Schwartzheim an' Hick was a Corman frind iv his an' he wint down to see that no injustice was done him. "Did he ask ye to go?" ast th' coort. "No," says th' pris'ner, "but me prestige as a slugger wud be in danger if I didn't go over an' punch this here little man," he says. "Niver, niver shud it be said that a German citizen shan't be able to collect his debts annywhere but in Germany," he says. "Th' mailed fist," he says, "gits there first—" "No more iv that," says th' judge. "This is a coort iv law. Hohenzollern ye're a dangerous man. Ye're noisy, ritous an' offinsive. I'm determined to make an example iv ye, an' sintince ye to stay in Germany f'r th' rest iv ye'er nachral life, an' may th' Lord have mercy on ye'er sowl. As f'r ye, Edwards, ye're even worse. I will hold ye without bail ontil th' polis can collect all their ividence again' ye. Casthro, ye're discharged. Th' worst thing I cud think iv doin' to ye is to sind ye back to ye'er beautiful Vinzwala." Th' pris'ner Hohenzollern made a dimonsthration

while bein' raymoved fr'm th' dock. It is undherstud
that Edward or Edwards has offered to tell all he
knows, an' promises to implicate siv'ral prominent
parties.'

"That's th' way I thought 'twud be. Be hivins,
Hinnissy, I looked forward to th' day whin if a king,
impror or czar started a rough house th' blue bus
wud come clangin' through th' sthreets an' they'd
be hauled off to Holland f'r thrile. I looked to see
th' United States sinit pulled ivry month or two, an'
all th' officers iv th' navy fugitives fr'm justice. I
thought th' coort wud have a kind iv a bridewell
built where they'd sind th' internaytional dhrunks
an' disordhilies, an' where ye cud go anny day an'
see Willum Hohenzollern cooperin' a bar'l, an' me
frind Joe Chamberlain peggin' shoes, while gr-reat
war iditors, corryspondints, statesmen, an' other
disturbers iv th' peace walked around in lock shtep,
an' th' keeper iv th' jail showed ye a book filled with
photygrafts iv th' mos' notoryous iv thim: 'Number
two thousan' an' wan, Joe Chamberlain, profissional
land grabber, five years,' or 'Willum Hohenzollern,
all-round ruffyan, life.' That wud be th' fine day
whin th' wagon wud be backed up in fr-ront iv th'
partlymints iv th' wurruld an' th' bull-pen wud be
full iv internaytional grafters, get-rich-quick op'ra-
tors an' short ar-rm men, whin th' Monroe docthrine
wud be condimned as a public nuisance. But it
hasn't come. Th' coort is there, noddin' over th'
docket jus' like a coort, while outside th' rowdies
ar-re shootin' at each other, holdin' up Chinymen an'

naygurs, pickin' pockets, blowin' safes an' endangerin' th' lives iv dacint people. They'se a warrant out f'r Bill Hohenzollern, but they'se no wan to sarve it. He's on th' rampage, breakin' windows an' chasin' people over th' roofs, while Edward or Edwards stands around th' corner, waitin' f'r th' goods to be delivered, an savin' his ammunytion to use it on his pal, if they quarrel over th' divide. There's th' internaytional coort, ye say, but I say, where ar-re th' polis. A coort's all r-right enough, but no coort's anny good onless it is backed up be a continted constabulary, it's counthry's pride, as th' pote says. Th' czar iv Rooshya didn't go far enough. Wan good copper with a hickory club is worth all th' judges between Amsterdam and Rotterdam. I want to see th' day whin jus' as Bill Hohenzollern an' Edward or Edwards meets on th' corner an' prepares a raid on a laundhry, a big polisman will step out iv a dure an' say: 'I want ye, Bill, an' ye might as well come along quite.' But I suppose it wud be jus' th' same thing as it is now in rale life."

"How's that?" asked Mr. Hennessy.'

"All th' biggest crooks wud get on th' polis foorce," said Mr. Dooley.

On Peace

"Well, sir," said Mr. Dooley, "whin I watched me frind Willum Jennings Bryan marchin' off to defind his counthry in th' year iv ninety-eight 'tis little I thought I'd live to see him such a champeen iv peace as he is today.

"O, but he was th' martial hayro in thim days. He didn't wait f'r his counthry to call him. If he had he'd be waitin' to this minyit f'r at that time Columbya was in th' hands iv freedom's inimies an' she refused to shriek f'r help fr'm anny but sthraight Republicans.

"No, sir; he didn't wait to be called, but he assimbled a rig'mint iv his own, th' Forty-fifth Nebrasky Foot, illicted himself colonel, got a soard fr'm Moses Oppenheim, th' well-known military outfitter iv Lincoln, climbed aboard ol' Dobbin, an' with a wild cheer led his men be a series iv foorced marches over th' Chat-talky cirket to Saint Joe, Missoury, where he threw up inthrenchmints an' waited f'r th' inimy to assail him.

"They didn't dare to.

"At th' close iv th' dhreadful sthruggle he hon'-rably discharged himsilf an' returned to lecturin', runnin' f'r prisidint, an' th' other peaceful pursoots iv private life.

"That's a long time ago, but iver since when th' vethrans iv Chickamaha an' Tampy gather around th' pool table to discuss th' rations an' other horrors iv th' conflict, no name is more often on their lips thin th' name iv th' prisint an' sometimes absint sicrety iv state.

"Now, I say that whin a man like this, a man who has seen war, a man who has smelled powdher without sneezin', a man who not wanst but manny times has slept out iv dures in a tent, a man who has known th' misery iv ridin' on a horse, comes out as

D—9

an advycate iv peace ye might as well sind th' dogs iv war to th' pound. They'll niver bite again.

"It didn't make much diff'rence so long as 'twas on'y Andhrew Carnaygie, f'r ivry wan knows he's a man iv peace that niver harmed a hair iv annybody or annything but th' English language.

"But whin a rale martial hayro tur-rns again th' spoort it's all day with it.

"Says Colonel Willum Jennings Bryan iv th' Forty-fifth Nebrasky Foot, 'We'll have no more war,' he says, 'Peace, he says, 'will brood over th' wurruld like a hen,' he says.

" 'We'll build no more battleships,' he says, 'but instead we will sind out a fleet that will devastate th' wurruld with American love. We'll call wan ship "Harmony," an' another "Brotherly Love," an' another "Sweet Thoughts," an' another "Happy Dhreams."

" 'Do I hear anny suggistions fr'm th' aujeence f'r names? Th' little girl in blue in th' third row has an idee. What is it, little lady? Speak up, please! That's right. A very good name. Th' little lady suggists "Love Me Little, Love Me Long"—a very sweet an' appropriate name f'r a stanch ship iv our navy.

" 'Th' little boy in th' back iv th' hall raises his hand. Well, me little man, what name do ye propose? I mane you, th' little Christyan with th' red hair an' th' freckles.

"What's that? "Ate 'Em Alive"? O, no. No, no. I'm afraid it wudden't do. A pretty name, but not sooted to a flotilly that is to carry a message iv brotherhood to th' wurruld.

"Excuse me f'r a minyit, frinds; here's a messenger fr'm th' state departmint. What? Th' prisidint iv Mexico demands to be recognized? All right. I recognize him. I'd recognize him annywhere in th' dark as a half breed Indyan desperado. Tell him so f'r me, an' tell him further that if he wants anny more reconition fr'm me I'll ask me frind Joe Daniels to bounce a couple iv cannon balls off his head to show how well I know him.

" 'If that fellow realizes whin he's lucky he'll thry his best not to be reconized be anny wan that might turn him over to th' polis.

" 'But, kind frinds, as I was sayin' whin intherrupted be officyal business, we clasp th' whole wurruld to our bosom; we have no inimies; so why shud we go armed?

" 'We will convart our soards into prunes—that is, into prunin' hooks to chip th' ripe grape with its life givin' juice fr'm th' arbor iv peace.

" 'An fr'm th' guns iv our battleships will fly not shrapnel or chain shot, as at prisint, but roses an' vilets an' anymonies an' tender wurruds. I thank ye, I thank ye, I thank ye.'

"So I s'pose, Hinnissy, th' end has about come f'r that rude pastime that has amused th' young people iv th' wurruld iver since there was a wurruld where men bumped into each other.

"Th' on'y thing I'd like to know is what's goin' to take its place. It's an ancyent institootion, wan iv th' very oldest, this here business iv men fightin' each other. They seem to take more nachrally to it thin to embracin'.

"Th' first thing two little kids does afther they've made frinds is to slam each other. Whin a man is old an' all his frinds ar-re gone he still has plenty iv inimies left, ye can bet on that.

"Yes, sir; it's been goin' on f'r a long time, like most iv th' bad things iv th' wurruld. An' if it goes what ar-re we goin' to cillybrate if we don' cilly-brate war?

"Th' other day a lot iv ol' lads that had fought at th' battle iv Gettysburg wint back to look over th' field an' pint out to each other th' place where they'd shtud durin' Pickett's charge.

"They'd meet together an' wan ol' fellow wud go up to a perfect sthranger an' say: 'Ain't ye th' Jawnny Reb that I had th' saber dool with on th' hill?'

"An' says th' other: 'Well, I vow if ye ain't th' Yank that I carrid on me back to th' ol' barn afther I'd martally wounded ye.'

" 'Sure I am; an' d'ye remimber how whin ye lay dyin' I crawled on me hands an' knees to th' well an' fetched ye wather in a goord?'

"An' so they go on gossipin', an' it don't make anny diff'rence if this is th' first time in their lives they've iver clapped eyes on each other, th' feelin' is just th' same.

"An' they hobble away an' have a toddy or maybe a sunsthroke together, an' ye'd think fr'm th' way th' southren ol' fellow talks that if Longsthreet had listened to him Jeff Davis wud've had his feet on th' desk at th' White House th' day afther th' battle, an' fr'm th' way th' northern ol' fellow talks that if Meade had let him he wud've pursooed th' flyin' rebels single handed an' ended th' war there an' thin.

"Th' thruth is, iv coorse, fifty years ago they were nawthin' but two little boys poppin' away with guns as fast as they cud on th' Foorth iv July, with no polisman to stop thim.

"I know, because me cousin Mike was at th' battle iv Gettysburg. To hear him tell it he was th' on'y wan on th' union side, th' rest iv th' army havin' run away an' left him alone.

"An' he wud've been defeated at that if he hadn't stopped firin', f'r he was a poor shot. But he bethought himsilf iv usin' th' butt end iv th' musket, which was more nachral, an' th' carnage was dhreadful.

"He always told me he niver spint a more injyable day in his life, an' I invied him, f'r I sarved me counthry in thim throublous times be dhrivin' a thruck, an occypation akelly dangerous but with little glory to it.

"I r-read about these Gettysburg vethrans with a tear runnin' down me nose, but d'ye suppose I cud get up anny enthusyasm at a reunion iv th' Thruck Dhrivers iv Sixty-three if some other ol' vethran come up to me an' said, 'Ar-ren't ye th' hayro that lost th' bill iv ladin' on Canal sthreet?' or 'D'ye remimber whin ye dhropped th' crate iv wathermilons at Pier Six?' No, sir.

"An', be Hivens, I can't think iv a crowd iv th' survivors iv th' campaign iv ninety-six gettin' together an' wan iv thim sayin,' 'There's where I lost me vote,' an' another, 'There's where I lost me hearin'.' I cudden't cheer. I wint through that awful sthruggle an' suffered much, but I refuse to cillybrate it.

"It's a sthrange thing to me, Hinnissy, that with ivry wan boostin' peace there's so little iv it in th' wurruld. There've been peace congresses an' wars goin' on side be side iver since I can remimber. There's niver anny peace annywhere excipt afther a war.

"Whin a nation is at peace it's thinkin' iv war, an' whin it's at war it's thinkin' iv peace. In time iv war, as Hogan says, prepare f'r peace.

"Th' most money iver given to th' cause iv peace come fr'm a German man, lasteways I think he was a German man, that'd made his bundle sellin' stuff to blow up armies in time iv war.

"Accordin' to th' will iv this Quaker, th' fellow in all th' wurruld that does most f'r th' cause iv peace gets a bunch iv money. Well, who d'ye think it was grabbed off th' first prizes? Was it Willum Jennings? Or Andhrews? It was not.

"Wan purse wint to that gintle little pote Roodyard Kipling, author iv th' tender sonnet entitled, 'Slay,Slay,Slay." An' another was handed over to no less a dovelike charackter thin our own Tidy. An' so it goes.

"Wan iv th' gr-reatest peace advycates is Schwartzmeister's Impror Willum. An' how does he advycate it, tell me? He dhresses himsilf up in a unyform, puts a brass pot on his head, has th' hired man get out th' bicycle pump an' blow up his chest, an' thin he sthrides up an' down th' frontier shakin' his fist at wan an' all an' invitin' thim to come on.

"An' he gets nawthin' but peace. His granfather that was a gintle soul was at war most iv th' time, but this la-ad has sawed nawthin' but air with his soard. He is champeen iv th' wurruld be default. Like as not he'll go to his grave without iver seein' a modhren cannon used f'r anny other purpose thin to salute him.

"I don't know whether Willum Jennings Bryan will have his way or not, but it looks to me, Hinnissy, as though orators wud go on talkin' peace an' blacksmiths makin' cannons ontil th' end iv time. I like to hear th' peace talk, but I'm more comfortable listenin' to it if me ear catches in th' distance th' sound iv th' anvil.

"In me long expeeryence I've found that th' love iv a fight is in near ivry man an' that there's th' makin' iv a first class quarrel whiniver anny two people get within' sthrikin' distance iv each other.

"Faith, how can I think nations will stay at peace whin I see how it is with mesilf? I go out iv a fine, pleasant mornin', feelin' on th' best iv terms with all th' wurruld. I hum a little song, I smile an' bow to me frinds, an' I think to mesilf how kind ar-re all th' faces I see around me. How cud anny wan fight

with thim agreeable people? There isn't th' thrace
iv a scrap in me. 'Tra-la-la,' says I, gettin' on a
sthreet car.

"An' thin a janyal lookin' sthranger steps on me
foot—accidentally, d'ye mind? Do I appeal to th'
conductor to ask has me honor been injured? Faith,
I do not. I make me declaration iv war an' swing on
him at th' same time, an' afther we've had it out we
dhraw up a threaty iv peace an' apologize, an' th'
next time he's careful where he puts his foot. An'
so it is with nations."

"I shud think," said Mr. Hennessy, "that sinsible
nations cud always arbytrate annything."

"They cud," said Mr. Dooley, "but d'ye think a lot
iv foolish people ar-re anny less foolish than anny
wan iv thim?

"Besides I ain't sure that a fight ain't sometimes
betther thin a lawsuit. It laves less hard feelin'."

On International Amenities

" 'Fellow subjicks,' says th' sicrety iv state [John
Hay], 'diplomacy is far diff'rent business thin it
used to be. (A voice, 'Good f'r you.') In th' days iv
Bismarck, Gladstun an' Charles Francis Adams
'twas a case iv inthrigue an' deceit. Now it is as simple as sellin' a pair iv boots. In fifteen years th'
whole nature iv man is so changed that a diplomat
has on'y to be honest, straight-forward an' manly
an' concede ivrything an' he will find his opponents
will meet him half way an' take what he gives. Un-
forchunitly diplomacy on'y goes as far as the dure.

It is onable to give protection to th' customer, so whin he laves th' shop th' sthrong arm men iv th' Sinit knocks him down an' takes fr'm him ivrything he got inside an' more too. Di-plomacy has become a philanthropic pursoot like shop-keepin', but politics, me lords, is still th' same ol' spoort iv highway robb'ry. But I done what I cud to protict th' intherests iv th' mother, father an' brother-in-law counthry, an' between you an' me if I don't desarve th' Victorya cross f'r presintin' that threaty to th' Sinit nobody does, I will on'y say that hinceforth th' policy iv this gover'mint will be as befure not to bully a sthrong power or wrong a weak, but will remain thrue to th' principle iv wrongin' th' sthrong an' bullyin' th' weak.'

European Intervention

"That's goin' to be th' unixpicted blow iv anny war that th' parishes iv Europe wages again' us. They will decline to eat. They will turn back our wheat an' pork an' short rib sides. They'll starve us out. If left to their own resoorces, Europe cud outstarve America in a month."

"I'm not afraid iv thim," said Mr. Hennessy. "Whin I was a young man, I cud take a runnin' jump acrost Germany or France, an' as f'r England we'd hardly thrip over it in th' dark."

"Perhaps ye're right," said Mr. Dooley. "But if all thim gr-reat powers, as they say thimsilves, was f'r to attack us, d'ye know what I'd do? I'll tell ye. I'd blockade Armour an' Comp'ny an' th' wheat ilivators iv Minnysoty. F'r, Hinnissy, I tell ye, th' hand that rocks th' scales in th' grocery store, is th' hand that rules th' wurruld."

War and War Makers

"Thrue f'r ye," said Mr. Dooley," an' that's why I wisht it cud be fixed up so's th' men that starts th' wars could do th' fightin'. Th' throuble is that all th' prelimin'ries is arranged be matchmakers an' all they'se left f'r fighters is to do th' murdherin'. A man's got a good job at home an' he wants to make it sthrongor. How can he do it? Be throwin' out some one that's got an akelly good job down th' sthreet. Now he don't go over as I wud an' say, 'Here Schwartzmeister (or Kruger as th' case may be) I don't like ye'er appearance, ye made a monkey iv me in argymint befure th' neighborhood an' if ye continyue in business ye'll hurt me thrade, so here goes to move ye into th' sthreet!' Not that la-ad. He gets a crowd around him an' says he: 'Kruger (or Schwartzmeister as th' case may be) is no good. To begin with he's a Dutchman. If that ain't enough he's a cantin', hymn singin' murdhrous wretch that wuddent lave wan iv our counthrymen ate a square meal if he had his way. I'll give ye all two dollars a week if ye'll go over an' desthroy him.' An' th' other la-ad, what does he do? He calls in th' neighbors an' says he: 'Dooley is sindin' down a gang iv savages to murdher me. Do ye lave ye'er wurruk an' ye'er families an' rally ar-round me an' where ye see me plug hat wave do ye go in th' other direction,' he says, 'an' slay th' brutal inimy,' he says. An' off goes th' sojers an' they meet a lot iv la-ads that look like thimsilves an' makes sounds that's more or less human an' ates out iv plates an' they swap smokin' tobacco an' sings songs together an' th' next day they're up early jabbing holes in each other with baynits. An' whin its all over they'se me an' Chamberlain at home victoryous an' Kruger an' Schwartzmeister at home akelly victoryous. An' they make me prime minister or aldherman but whin I want a man to put in me coal I don't take wan with a wooden leg.

"I'll niver go down again to see sojers off to th' war. But ye'll see me at th' depot with a brass band whin th' men that causes wars starts f'r th' scene iv carnage. Whin Congress goes forth to th' sun-kissed an' rain jooled isles iv th' Passyfic no more heartier cheer will be heard thin th' wan or two that rises fr'm th' bosom iv Martin Dooley. Says I, give thim th' chanst to make histhry an' lave th' young men come home an' make car wheels. If Chamberlain likes war so much 'tis him that ought to be down there in South Africa peltin' over th' road with ol' Kruger chasin' him with a hoe. Th' man that likes fightin' ought to be willin' to turn in an' spell his fellow-counthrymen himsilf. An' I'd even go this far an' say that if Mack wants to subjoo th' Ph'lippeens — —"

"Ye're a thraitor," said Mr. Hennessy.

"I know it," said Mr. Dooley, complacently.

"Ye're an anti-expansionist."

"If ye say that again," cried Mr. Dooley, angrily, "I'll smash in ye'er head."

POLITICS—A BRANCH OF THE LAW

Business and Political Honesty

"It's a shame," said Mr. Dooley, laying down his paper, "that more business men don't go into pollyticks."

"I thought they did," said Mr. Hennessy.

"No, sir," said Mr. Dooley; "ye don't r-read th' pa-apers. Ivry year, whin th' public conscience is aroused as it niver was befure, me frinds on th' palajeems iv our liberties an' records iv our crimes calls f'r business men to swab out our govermint with business methods. We must turn it over to pathrites who have made their pile in mercantile pursoots iv money whereiver they cud find it. We must injooce th' active, conscientious young usurers fr'm Wall Sthreet to take an inthrest in public affairs. Th' poolrooms is open. To thim guilded haunts iv vice th' poor wurrukinman carries his weekly wage, an' thries to increase it enough so that he can give it to his wife without blushin'. Down with th' poolrooms, says I. But how? says you. Be ilictin' a business man mayor, says I. But who'll we get? says you. Who bether, says I, thin th' prisidint iv th' Westhren Union Tillygraft Comp'ny, who knows where th' poolrooms ar-re.

"Th' wather departmint is badly r-run. Ilict th' prisidint iv th' gas comp'ny. Th' onforchnit sthreet railroads have had thimsilves clutched be th' throat be a corrupt city council an' foorced to buy twenty millyon dollars' worth iv sthreets f'r sixty-four wan-hundherd dollar bills. Oh, f'r a Moses to lead us

out of th' wilderness an' clane th' Augeenyan sta-
bles an' steer us between Silly an' What's-it's-name
an' hoist th' snow-white banner iv civic purity an'
break th' feathers that bind a free people an' seize
th' hellum iv state fr'm th' pi-ratical crew an' restore th' heritage iv our fathers an' cleanse th' stain
fr'm th' fair name iv our gr-reat city an' cure th'
evils iv th' body pollytick an' cry havic an' let loose
th' dogs iv war an'—captain th' uprisin' iv honest
manhood again th' cohorts iv corruption an' shake
off th' collar riveted on our necks be tyrannical
bosses an' prim'ry rayform? Where is Moses?
Where is this all-around Moses, soldier, sailor, lock-
smith, doctor, stable-boy, polisman, an' disinfect-
ant? Where else wud such a vallyble Moses be
thin in th' bank that owns th' sthreet railroads? If
Moses can't serve we'll r-run his lawyer, th' gr-reat
pollytickal purist, th' Hon'rable Ephraim Duck, author iv "Duck on Holes in th' Law", "Duck on Flaws
in th' Constitution", "Duck on Ivry Man has His
Price", "Duck's First Aid to th' Suspicted", "Duck's
Iliminthry Lessons in Almost Crime", "Th' Supreem
Coort Made Easy", or "Ivry Man his Own Allybi"
and so on. Where is Judge Duck? He's down at
Springfield, doin' a little ligislative law business f'r
th' gas comp'ny. Whin he comes up he'll be glad to
lead th' gr-reat annyooal battle f'r civic purity.
Hurrah f'r Duck an' Freedom, Duck an' Purity,
Duck an' th' Protiction iv th' Rights iv Property,
Duck an' Fearless Compromise.

"Befure our most illusthrees life-insurance solici-

tor rose in th' wurruld, whin he was merely prisidint iv th' United States, th' on'y way we cud dig a
job out iv him f'r a good dimmycrat was to form th'
Sixth Ward Chamber iv Commerce an' indorse th'
candydate. Whin Cohen first wint to Wash'nton to
have Schmitt appinted Counsul at Chefoo, th' chief
ixicutive, as Hogan says, nearly brained him with a
paperweight marked J. P. M. But whin he wint
down as prisidint iv th' Ar-rchey Road Chamber iv
Commerce th' gr-reat man fell on his neck an' near
broke it. Th' frindship iv th' gr-reat, Hinnissy, is
worse thin their inmity. Their hathred sometimes
misses fire, but their frindship always lands in an
unguarded an' vital spot. This here Chamber iv
Commerce r-run th' pathronage iv th' disthrict f'r
a year. It used to meet in me back room till th' merchant princes got too noisy over a dice game an' I
put thim into th' sthreet.

"Yes, Hinnissy, me ideel iv a gr-reat statesman is
a grocer with elastic bands on his shirt-sleeves, ladlin' public policies out iv a bar'l with a wooden scoop.
How much betther wud Wash'nton an' Lincoln have
been if they'd known enough to inthrajooce business
methods into pollyticks. George was a good man, but
he niver thought iv settlin' th' throuble be compro-
misin' on a job as colonyal governor. He raised th'
divvle with property, so much so, be Hivins, that no
gr-reat financier to this day can tell what belongs
to him an' what belongs to some wan else. An'
there's Lincoln. What a little business thrainin'
wud've done f'r him! Look at th' roon he brought

on property be his carelessness. Millyons iv thim become worthless except as fuel f'r bonfires in th' Sunny Southland.

"It's a sthrange people can't see it th' way I do. There's Jawn Cassidy. Ye know him. He's a pollytician or grafter. The' same thing. His graft is to walk downtown to th' City Hall at eight o'clock ivry mornin' an' set on a high stool ontil five in th' afthernoon addin' up figures. Ivry week twenty dollars iv th' taxpayers' money, twinty dollars wrung fr'm you an' me, Hinnissy, is handed to this boodler. He used to get twinty-five in a clothin'-store, but he is a romantic young fellow, an' he thought 'twud be a fine thing to be a statesman. Th' diff'rence between a clothin' clerk an' a statesman clerk is that th' statesman clerk gets less money, an' has th' privilege iv wurrukin' out iv office hours. Well, Cassidy come in wan night with his thumbs stained fr'm his unholy callin'. 'Well,' says I, 'ye grafters ar-re goin' to be hurled out,' I says. 'I suppose so,' says he. 'We'll have a business administhration,' says I. 'Well,' says he, 'I wondher what kind iv a business will it be,' says he. 'Will it be th' insurance business? I tell ye if they iver inthrajooce life-insurance methods in our little boodle office there'll be a rivolution in this here city. Will it be a railroad administhration, with th' office chargin' ye twice as much f'r water as Armour pays? Will it be th' bankin' business, with th' prisidint takin' th' money out iv th' dhrawer ivry night an' puttin' in a few kind wurruds on a slip iv paper?

" 'What kind iv a business ar-re ye goin' to use to purify our corrupt govermint? Look here,' says he. 'I'm goin' out iv pollyticks,' he says. 'Me wife can't stand th' sthrain iv seein' th' newspapers always referrin' to me be a nickname in quotation marks. I've got me old job back, an' I've quit bein' a statesman,' he says. 'But let me tell ye something. I've been a boodler an' a grafter an' a public leech f'r five years, but I used to be a square business man, an' I'm givin' ye th' thruth whin I say that business ain't got a shade on pollyticks in th' matther iv honesty. Th' bankers was sthrong again' Mulcahy. But I know all about th' banks. Whin I was in th' clothin' business Minzenheimer used to have th' banks over-certify his checks ivry night. That wud mean two years in th' stir-bin f'r a pollytician, but I don't see no bankers doin' th' wan-two in th' iron gall'ries at Joliet. I knew a young fellow that wurruked in a bank, an' he told me th' prisidint sold th' United State Statutes to an ol' book dealer to make room f'r a ticker in his office. We may be a tough gang over at th' City Hall. A foreign name always looks tough whin its printed in a reform iditoryal. But, thank th' Lord, no man iver accused us iv bein' life-insurance prisidints. We ain't buncoin' an' scarin' people with th' fear iv death into morgedgin' their furniture to buy booze an' cigars f'r us,' he says. 'We may take bribes, because we need th' money, but we don't give thim because we want more thin we need. We're grafters, ye say, but there's manny a dollar pushed over th' counter iv a bank that Mul-

chay wud fling in th' eye iv th' man that offered it
to him.

" 'Th' pollytician grafts on th' public an' his inimies. It don't seem anny worse to him thin winnin'
money on a horse-race. He doesn't see th' writhin'
iv th' man he takes th' coin fr'm. But these here
high fi-nanciers grafts on th' public an' their inimies,
but principally on their frinds. Dump ye'er pard-
ner is th' quickest way to th' money. Mulcahy wud
rather die thin skin a frind that had sthrung a bet
with him. But if Mulcahy was a railroad boss instead
iv a pollytical boss he wud first wurruk up th' con-
fidence iv his frinds in him, thin he wud sell thim
his stock, thin he wud tell thim th' road was goin'
to th' dogs, an' make thim give it back to him f'r
nawthin'; thin he wud get out a fav'rable report,
an' sell th' stock to thim again. An' he'd go on doin'
this till he'd made enough to be ilicted prisidint iv
a good govermint club. Some iv th' boys down at our
office are owners iv stock. Whin do they first larn
that things ar-re goin' wrong with th' comp'ny?
Afther th' prisidint an' boord iv di-rectors have sold
out.

" 'Don't ye get off anny gas at me about business
men an' pollyticians. I niver knew a pollytician to
go wrong ontil he'd been contaminated be contact
with a business man. I've been five years in th' wather office, an' in all that time not a postage-stamp
has been missed. An' we're put down as grafters.
What is pollytical graft, annyhow? It ain't stealin'
money out iv a dhrawer. It ain't robbin' th' taxpayer

D—10

direct, th' way th' gas comp'ny does. All there's to it is a business man payin' less money to a pollytician thin he wud have to pay to th' city if he bought a sthreet or a dock direct.

" 'Iv coorse, there ar-re petty larceny grabs be polismen. That's so ivrywhere. Wheriver there's polisman there's a shake-down. But in ivry big crooked job there's a business man at wan end. Th' ligislachures is corrupt, but who makes it worth while f'r thim to be corrupt but th' pathrites iv th' life-insurance comp'nies? Th' la-ads in th' council ar-re out f'r th' stuff, says ye. But how do they make annything except be sellin' sthreets to th' high fi-nanceers that own th' railroad comp-nies? If business men niver wanted to buy things cheap that don't belong to thim no pollytician that cud carry a precinct wud go into th' council. I'm goin' back to business. Minzenheimer thinks he will need me to get th' aldherman to let him add fifty illegal feet to th' front iv his store. I'm goin' back to business, an' I expect to help purify it. What th' business iv this counthry needs,' he says, 'is f'r active young pollyticians to take an inthrest in it an' ilivate it to a higher plane. Me battle-cry is: "Honest pollytical methods in th' administhration iv business," ' he says 'In time,' he says, 'I hope to see th' same honesty, good faith, an' efficiency in th' Life Insurance Comp'nies an' th' Thrusts that we see now,' he says, 'in th' administhration iv Tammany Hall,' he says."

"There's a good deal in that," said Mr. Hennessy. "I knew an aldherman wanst that was honest as th' sun, except whin th' sthreet railroad or th' gas comp'ny needed something."

"Well, there ye ar-re," said Mr. Dooley. "It seems to me that th' on'y thing to do is to keep pollyticians an' business men apart. They seem to have a bad infloonce on each other. Whiniver I see an aldherman an' a banker walkin' down th' sthreet together I know th' Recordin' Angel will have to ordher another bottle iv ink."

Hanging Aldermen

Chicago is always on the point of hanging some one and quartering him and boiling him in hot pitch, and assuring him that he has lost the respect of all honorable men. Rumors of a characteristic agitation had come faintly up Archey Road, and Mr. Hennessy had heard of it.

"I hear they're goin' to hang th' aldhermen," he said. "If they thry it on Willum J. O'Brien, they'd betther bombard him first. I'd hate to be th' man that'd be called to roll with him to his doom. He cud lick th' whole Civic Featheration."

"I believe ye," said Mr. Dooley. "He's a powerful man. But I hear there is, as ye say, what th' pa-apers 'd call a movement on fut f'r to dec'rate Chris'mas threes with aldhermen, an' 'tis wan that ought to be encouraged. Nawthin' cud be happyer, as Hogan says, thin th' thought iv cillybratin' th' season be sthringin' up some iv th' fathers iv th' city where th' childher cud see thim. But I'm afraid, Hinnissy, that you an' me won't see it. 'Twill all be over soon, an' Willum J. O'Brien'll go by with his head just as near his shoulders as iver. 'Tis har-rd to hang an aldherman, annyhow. Ye'd have to suspind most iv thim be th' waist.

"Man an' boy, I've been in this town forty year an' more; an' divvle th' aldherman have I see hanged yet, though I've sthrained th' eyes out iv me head watchin' f'r wan iv thim to be histed anny pleasant mornin'. They've been goin' to hang thim wan week an' presintin' thim with a dimon' star th' next iver since th' year iv th' big wind, an' there's jus' as manny iv thim an' jus' as big robbers as iver there was.

" 'An' why shud they hang thim, Hinnissy? Why shud they? I'm an honest man mesilf, as men go. Ye might have ye'er watch, if ye had wan, on that bar f'r a year, an' I'd niver touch it. It wudden't be worth me while. I'm an honest man. I pay me taxes, whin Tim Ryan isn't assessor with Grogan's boy on th' books. I do me jooty; an' I believe in th' polis foorce, though not in polismen. That's diff'rent. But honest as I am, between you an' me, if I was an aldherman, I wudden't say, be hivins, I—think I'd stand firm; but—well if some wan come to me an' said, 'Dooley, here's fifty thousan' dollars f'r ye'er vote to betray th' sacred inthrests iv Chicago,' I'd go to Father Kelly an' ask th' prayers iv th' congregation.

" 'Tis not, Hinnissy, that this man Yerkuss goes up to an aldherman an' says out sthraight, 'Here, Bill, take this bundle, an' be an infamyous scoundhrel.' That's th' way th' man in Mitchigan Avnoo sees it, but 'tis not sthraight. D'ye mind Dochney that was wanst aldherman here? Ye don't. Well, I do. He ran a little conthractin' business down be Halsted Sthreet. 'Twas him build th' big shed f'r th' ice comp'ny. He was a fine man an' a sthrong wan. He begun his political career be lickin' a plasthrer be th' name iv Egan, a man that had th' County Clare thrip an' was thought to be th' akel iv anny man in town. Fr'm that he growed till he bate near ivry man he knew, an' become very pop'lar, so that he was sint to th' council. Now Dochney was an honest an' sober man whin he wint in; but wan day a man come up to him, an' says he, 'Ye know that ordhnance Schwartz inthrajooced?' 'I do,' says Dochney, 'an I'm again it. 'Tis a swindle,' he says. "Well," says th' la-ad, 'they'se five thousan' in it f'r ye,' he says. They had to pry Dochney off iv him. Th' nex' day a man he knowed well come to Dochney, an' says he, 'That's a fine ordhnance iv Schwartz.' 'It is, like hell,' says Dochney. ' 'Tis a plain swindle,' he says. ' 'Tis a good thing f'r th' comp'nies,' says this man; 'but look what they've done f'r th' city,' he says, 'an think,' he says, 'iv th' widdies an' orphans,' he says, 'that has their har-rd-earned coin invisted,' he says. An' a tear rolled down his cheek. 'I'm an orphan mesilf,' says Dochney; 'an' as f'r th' widdies, anny healthy widdy with sthreet-car stock ought to be ashamed iv hersilf if she's a widdy long,' he says. An th' man wint away.

"Now Dochney thought he'd put th' five thousan'

out iv his mind, but he hadn't. He'd on'y laid it by, an' ivry time he closed his eyes he thought iv it. 'Twas a shame to give th' comp'nies what they wanted, but th' five thousan' was a lot iv money. 'Twud lift th' morgedge. 'Twud clare up th' notes on th' new conthract. 'Twud buy a new dhress f'r Mrs. Dochney. He begun to feel sorrowful f'r th widdies an' orphans. 'Poor things'.' says he to himsilf, says he. 'Poor things, how they must suffer!' he says; 'an' I need th' money. Th' sthreet-car comp'nies is robbers,' he says; 'but 'tis thrue they've built up th' city,' he says, 'an' th' money'd come in handy,' he says. 'No wan'd be hurted, annyhow,' he says; 'an', sure, it ain't a bribe f'r to take money f'r doin, something ye want to do, annyhow,' he says. 'Five thousan' widdies an' orphans,' he says; an he wint to sleep.

"That was th' way he felt whin he wint down to see ol' Simpson to renew his notes, an' Simpson settled it. 'Dochney,' he says. 'I wisht ye'd pay up,' he says. 'I need th' money,' he says. 'I'm afraid th' council won't pass th' Schwartz ordhnance,' he says; 'an it manes much to me,' he says. 'Be th' way,' he says, 'how're ye goin' to vote on that ordhnance?' he says. 'I dinnaw,' says Dochney. 'Well,' says Simpson (Dochney tol' me this himsilf), 'whin ye find out, come an' see me about th' notes,' he says. An' Dochney wint to th' meetin'; an', whin his name was called, he hollered 'Aye,' so loud a chunk iv plaster fell out iv th' ceilin' an' stove in th' head iv a rayform aldherman."

"Did they hang him?" asked Mr. Hennessey.

"Faith, they did not," said Mr. Dooley. "He begun missin' his jooty at wanst. Aldherman always
do that after th' first few weeks. 'Ye got ye'er
money,' says Father Kelly; 'an' much good may it
do ye,' he says. 'Well,' says Dochney, 'I'd be a long
time prayin' mesilf into five thousan',' he says. An'
he become leader in th' council. Th' las' ordhnance
he inthrojooced was wan establishin' a license f'r
churches, an' compellin' thim to keep their fr-ront
dure closed an' th' blinds drawn on Sundah. He was
expelled fr'm th' St. Vincent de Pauls, an' ilicted a
director iv a bank th' same day.

"Now, Hinnissy, that there man niver knowed he
was bribed—th' first time. Th' second time he knew.
He ast f'r it. An' I wudden't hang Dochney. I
wudden't if I was sthrong enough. But some day
I'm goin' to let me temper r-run away with me, an'
get a comity together, an' go out an' hang ivry dam
widdy an' orphan between th' rollin' mills an' th'
foundlin's' home. If it wasn't f'r thim raypechious
crathers, they'd be no boodle annywhere."

"Well, don't forget Simpson," said Mr. Hennessy.

"I won't," said Mr. Dooley. "I Won't."

Making a Cabinet or the Spoils System at Work

"I suppose, Jawn," said Mr. Dooley, "ye do be
afther a governmint job. Is it council to Athlone or
what, I dinnaw?"

"I haven't picked out the place yet," said Mr. Mc-
Kenna. "Bill wrote me the day after election about

it. He says: 'John,' he says, 'take anything you want
that's not nailed to the wall,' he says. He heard of
my good work in the Twenty-ninth. We rolled up
eight votes in Carey's precinct, and had five of them
counted; and that's more of a miracle than carrying
New York by three hundred thousand."

"It is so," said Mr. Dooley. "It is f'r a fact. Ye
must 'v give the clerks an' judges morphine, an' ye
desarve great credit. Ye ought to have a place; an'
I think ye'll get wan, if there's enough to go round
among th' Irish Raypublicans. 'Tis curious what an
effect an illction has on th' Irish Raypublican vote.
In October an Irish Raypublican's so rare people
point him out on th' sthreet, an' women carry their
babies to see him. But th' day afther iliction, glory
be, ye run into thim ivrywhere,—on th' sthreet-car,
in the sthreet, in saloons principally, an' at th' meetin's iv th' Raypublican Comity. I've seen as manny
iv them as twinty in here to-day, an' ivry wan iv
thim fit to run anny job in th' govermint, fr'm di-
rectin' th' Departmint iv State to carryin' ashes out
an' dumpin thim in th' white lot.

"They can't all have jobs, but they've got to be attinded to first; an', whin Mack's got through with
thim, he can turn in an' make up that cabinet iv
his. Thin he'll have throuble iv his own, th' poor
man, on'y comin' into fifty thousand a year and rint
free. If 'twas wan iv th' customs iv th' great raypublic iv ours, Jawn, f'r to appoint th' most competent men f'r th' places, he'd have a mighty small lot
f'r to pick fr'm. But, seein' that on'y thim is iligible

that are unfit, he has th' divvle's own time selectin'.
F'r Sicrety iv State, if he follows all iv what Casey
calls recent precidints, he's limited to ayether a
jack-leg counthry lawyer, that has set around
Washington f'r twinty years, pickin' up a dollar or
two be runnin' errands f'r a foreign imbassy, or a
judge that doesn't know whether th' city of
Booloogne-sure-Mere, where Tynan was pinched, is
in Boolgahria or th' County Cavan. F'r Sicrety iv
th' Threasury he has a choice iv three kinds iv proud
and incompetent financeers. He can ayether take a
bank president, that'll see that his little bank an' its
frinds doesn't get th' worst iv it, or a man that
cudden't maintain th' par'ty iv a counthry dhry-
good store long enough to stand off th' sheriff, or a
broken-down Congressman, that is full iv red liquor
half the year, an' has remorse settin' on his chest
th' other half.

"On'y wan class is iligible f'r Attorney-gin'ral. To
fill that job, a man's got to be a first-class thrust
lawyer. If he ain't, th' Lord knows what'll happen.
Be mistake he might prosecute a thrust some day,
an' th' whole counthry'll be rooned. He must be a
man competint f'r to avoid such pitfalls an' snares,
so 'tis th' rule f'r to have him hang on to his job
with th' thrust afther he gets to Washington. This
keeps him in touch with th' business inthersts.

"F'r Sicrety iv War, th' most like wan is some
good prisident iv a sthreet-car company. 'Tis exthra-
ordinney how a man learns to manage military affairs be auditin' thrip sheets an' rentin' signs in a

sthreet-car to chewin' gum imporyums. If Gin'ral
Washington iv sacred mimory 'd been under a good
sthreet-car Sicrety iv War, he'd've wore a bell punch
to ring up ivry time he killed a Hessian. He wud so,
an' they'd've kep' tab on him, an', if he thried
to wurruk a brother-in-law on thim, they'd give him
his time.

"F'r th' Navy Departmint ye want a Southern
Congressman fr'm th' cotton belt. A man that iver
see salt wather outside iv a pork bar'l be disquali-
fied f'r th' place. He must live so far fr'm th' sea
that he don't know a capstan bar fr'm a sheet an-
chor. That puts him in th' proper position to inspect
armor plate f'r th' imminent Carnegie, an' in-
sthruct admirals that's been cruisin' an' fightin' an'
dhrinkin' mint juleps f'r thirty years. He must
know th' difference bechune silo an' insilage, how to
wean a bull calf, an' th' best way to cure a spavin.
If he has that information, he is fixed f'r th' job.

"Whin he wants a good Postmaster-gin'ral, take
ye'er ol' law partner f'r awhile, an', be th' time he's
larned to stick stamps, hist him out, an' put in a
school-teacher fr'm a part iv th' counthry where
people communicate with each other through a
conch. Th' Sicrety iv th' Interior is an important
man. If possible, he ought to come fr'm Maine or
Florida. At anny rate, he must be a resident iv an
Atlantic seacoast town, an' niver been west iv Co-
hoes. If he gets th' idee there are anny white people
in Ann Arbor or Columbus, he loses his job.

"Th' last place on th' list is Sicrety iv Agriculture.

A good, lively business man that was born in th'
First Ward an' moved to th' Twenty-foorth after th'
fire is best suited to this office. Thin he'll have no
prejudices against sindin' a farmer cactus seeds
whin he's on'y lookin' f'r wheat. an' he will have a
proper understandin' iv th' importance iv an early
Agricultural Bureau rayport to th' bucket-shops.

"No Prisident can go far away that follows Cleveland's cabinet appintmints, although it may be
hard f'r Mack, bein' new at th' business, to select
th' right man f'r th' wrong place. But I'm sure he'll
be advised be his frinds, an' fr'm th' lists iv candy-
dates I've seen he'll have no throuble in findin' tim-
ber."

On Drink and Statesmanship

"Have a glass iv beer with me," said Mr. Hennessy. "What's that?" demanded Mr. Dooley.

"I said," Mr. Hennessey replied testily, "will ye
have a glass iv beer with me—an' on me—or won't
ye?"

"I will not," said Mr. Dooley. "How dare ye make
such a suggistion to me? If I thought ye had six
cints in ye'er clothes I'd sue ye f'r libel. I wud so.
I'll have ye to know that these secrit rumors that
ar-re circulatin' around about me dhrinkin habits
has got to stop.

"I do not dhrink beer, butthermilk, pop, ice crame
sody, sarsprilly, or tay in anny form. Whin much
fatigued be talkin' to ye I sometimes take a glass iv
brandy with a tayspoonful iv milk in it. But not
often, as I do not like th' taste iv milk.

"Whin I have a chill or thirst I dhrink modhrately iv a bucket or two iv whisky, brandy, rum, gin, karosene or gasolene. I niver take champagne excipt whin th' doctor ordhers it, an' if th' dock ordhers it he's got to pay f'r it, too. I niver dhrink champagne.

"An' there ye have in a few brief wurruds me innocent dhrinkin' habits."

"What ar-re ye talkin' about?" said Mr. Hennessy. "Ye nivir dhrink har'ly annything at all."

"I know it," said Mr. Dooley, "but I don't want it to get out. I'm thinkin' iv goin' back into pollyticks again, an' I want th' earnest dhrinkers iv th' counthry to feel that I'm wan iv thim. They're a large an' inflooinchal body iv men an' much niglicted.

"So if ye hear anny rumors in th' fash'nable clubs that ye frequint that I am not hon'rary prisidint iv th' Ancient Ordher iv Alcoholics, that I don't have th' pain killer piped into me while I sleep, or that me on'y physical exercise is not deleeryom thremens, I want ye to denounce thim as base, false, an' malicious.

"If they ask ye, 'Did ye iver smell his breath?' tell thim ye have, that ye cudden't help it, livin' in th' same sthreet.

"If they ask ye, 'Did ye detict th' prisince iv liquor?' tell thim that th' gusts fr'm me pipes is practically 90 percint pure benzine, with a tayspoonful or two iv breath added.

"Tell thim iv th' time ye found me on th' sthreet corner thryin' to dance a turkey throt with a lamp post. Tell thim iv the polismen I've bate.

"Let thim know that whin I go out iv town an' me frinds want to sind me home, which they always do, at once, they have to crate me up an' ship me be freight.

"Tell thim iv th' time ye see me hurl me boot at th' polky dot elephant that thried to get into bed with me. Here an' now, Hinnissy, I appoint ye me campaign manager.

"If ye do ye'er jooty I'll capture th' intire alcoholic vote, an', judgin' be what I see an' hear on illiction nights, that ought to land me aisy in anny office in our beloved fatherland.

"Sure, it's a sthrange change has come over our pollyticks since I was captain iv me precinct. We ar-re fallen, as Hogan says, on imminate days.

"Th' hardy and gloryous peeryod in th' histhry iv th' Republic has passed, an' th' times whin Hinnery Clay an' Dan'l Webster wud sit f'r hours pushin' th' scuttle to an' fro acrost th' table has gone to return no more. Booze an' iloquence has both passed out iv public life.

"No longer is th' gr-reat statesman carried to th' platform be loving hands an' lashed to th' raillin where him an' King Alcohol sings a duet on th' splindors iv th' blue sky an' th' onfadin' glories iv th' flag; but afther atin' a pepsin tablet an' sippin' a glass if light gray limonade he reads to th' assimbled multichood th' financial repoort iv th' Standard Ile Comp'ny f'r th' physical year endin' June first.

"Mind ye, all this was befure my time. In my day

I niver knew a gr-reat statesman that dhrank, or if he did he nivver landed anny job betther thin clerk in th' weather office. But as Hogan says Shakespere says, they pretinded a vice if they had it not.

"A pollytician was a baten man if th' story wint around that he was sildom seen dhrunk in public. His aim was to create an imprissyon that he was a gay fellow, a jovyal toss pot, that thought nawthin' iv puttin' a gallon iv paint into him durin' an avenin's intertainment.

"They had to exercise diplomacy, d'ye mind, to keep their repylations goin'. Whin Higgins was runnin' f'r sheriff he always ordhered gin an' I always give him water. Ye undherstand, don't ye? Ye know what gin looks like? Well, wather looks like gin.

"Wan day Gallagher took up his glass be mistake an' Higgins lost th' precinct be 40 votes.

"Sinitor O'Brien held a bolder coorse. He used to dump th' stuff on th' flure whin no wan was lookin' an' go home with a light foot while I swept out his constitooents.

"Yes, sir, I've seen him pour into th' sawdust quarts an' gallons iv me precious old Remorse Rye, aged be me own hands on th' premises.

"Th' most onpopylar Prisidint we iver had was Rutherford B. Hayes—an' why? Was it because he stole th' prisidincy away fr'm Sam'l J. Tilden? It was not. Anny wan wud stale a prisidincy fr'm a Dimmycrat in thim days an' think th' larceny was pathriotism.

"No, sir, 'twas because whin people wint up to th'

White House they got nawthin' to dhrink but spark-
lin' wather, a bivridge, Hinnissy, that is nayether
cheerin' nor ineebratin', but gives ye the most incon-
vanient part iv a deebauch, that is th' hiccups.

"Fr'm 8 o'clock, whin they set down to dinner, to
8:30, whin' th' last Southern Congressman ran
shriekin' down th' sthreet, this gr-reat but tactless
man pumped his guests full iv imprisoned gas.

"An' whin his term expired he wint back where
he come fr'm an' I niver heerd iv him again. Polly-
tickally speakin', d'ye mind, he wint down, as ye
might say, to a wathry grave.

"But it's all changed now, be hivens. Pollyticians
no longer come into me place. I'm glad iv it. I prefer
th' thrade iv prosp'rous steel mannyfacthrers like
ye'ersilf. It's more reg'lar.

"A statesman wud no more be seen goin into a
saloon thin he wud into a meetin' iv th' Anti-Semitic
league.

"Th' imprissyon he thries to give is that th' sight
iv a bock beer sign makes him faint with horror, an'
that he's stopped atin' bread because there's a certain amount iv alcohol concealed in it. He wishes to
brand as a calumy th' statement that his wife uses
an alcohol lamp to heat her curlin' irns.

"Ivry statesman in this broad land is in danger iv
gettin' wather-logged because whiniver he sees a
possible vote in sight he yells f'r a pitcher iv ice wather an' dumps into himsilf a basin iv that noble
flooid that in th' more rugged days iv th' republic
was on'y used to put out fires an' sprinkle th' lawn.

In thim days a thrue statesman wud no more think iv dhrinkin' wather than he wud of takin' a bath in a tubfull of beer.

"I pick up th' pa-aper an' r-read: 'Prisidint Wilson has ast th' corryspondints to deny th' mallicyous rumor circulated be th' preedytory inthrests that he takes vanilla ice crame in his sody wather. Th' Prisidint does not aven dhrink sody wather, excipt on a dhruggist's prescription. His fav'rite bivrage is skimmed milk.

' "Th' sinit havin' closed th' sinit bar as sinful has abolished th' Turkish bath as onnecessary.'

"William Jennings Bryan on his return to Wash'nton f'r a day's rest fr'm his arjoos jooties invited th' foreign abbassadures to attind a dinner an' announced that he wud give thim on'y pure an' onferminted juice iv th' grape to dhrink. Th' ambassadures held a hurried meetin' an' cabled to their home Govermints f'r insthructions. They were ordhered to attind in th' inthrests iv peace, but th' Fr-rinch ambassadure resigned.

"At th' dinner th' Sicrety iv State toasted peace in a dipper iv th' toothsome suds. In attimptin' to dhrink th' toast th' English ambassadure was attacked with a vilent coughin' spell an' was onable to respond, but was undhersthud to say that there was worse ways iv dyin' thin on th' field iv battle.

"In th' mist iv an otherwise joyous dinner th' German ambassadure turned suddenly pale an' complained iv a horrible pain in th' stomach. He was able to lave the festive boord an' be his own directions was assisted to a neighborin' ratskellar, where at 4 o'clock this mornin' he was restin' aisy.

"Whin th' dinner broke up at 9 o'clock th' guests were most enthusyastic, an' whin th' Jap'nese ministher proposed to sing 'F'r he's a jolly good fellow' siv'ral iv th' diplomats bust into tears.

" 'Misther Bryan was much plazed with th' success iv his innovation. He has dhrunk grape juice f'r manny years, sometimes consumin' as manny as 40 glasses a day. In fact, he sildom ates a piece iv pie without washin' it down with his fav'rite bivrage, onless pressed be business.

" 'Th' sicrety gathered th' corryspondints together yisterday afthernoon, an', givin' them each a glass iv grape juice, which they consumed ex officyo, asked thim to convey to th' wurruld th' news that it is undhersthud in officyal circles that th' Sicrety iv State has niver dhrunk booze, smoked or chewed tobacco, took snuff, swore, gambled, fought chickens or danced th' jelly glide.'

"To show ye how times has changed, there's me frind Tiddy Rosenfelt goes up to Michigan an' sues th' iditor iv a story-an'-a-half newspaper f'r libel f'r sayin' that he was well known to be a white hope among th' pethrolyum rasslers iv th' wurruld.

"If he'd been in pollyticks as long as I have an' was as active an' as prom'nent he wudn't have noticed th' insult. He'd know that in pollyticks th' worst men ar-re often libeled, so what can th' best expict?

"It's a good thing, too, f'r it keeps sinsitive

D—11

an' thin skinned men out iv public life an' dhrives thim into journalism.

"An' if he'd known all th' things that's been said about him be th' more substantial iv his fellow citizens he'd've sint this iditor a letter thankin' him f'r his support but askin' him not to overdo th' language iv flow'ry complimint.

"Whiniver he turned out a message to Congress an' a banker reached down in his jeans' an' found that th' dollar he'd put in there th' night befure was now on'y fifty cints, th' financeer wud assimble other financeers around him an' they'd discuss th' failures iv Tiddy Rosenfelt.

"He was this an' he was that. He niver shot a grizzly bear. It was notoryous that he pizened thim. He was not at th' battle iv San Joon Hill. Whin that affray was over he was discovered by a naygar throoper undher a wagon disguised as a Spanish grandee an' moanin' feebly, 'Take me home to Eyesther Bay.'

"'I've always known he was crazy,' says wan jaynial soul. 'F'r four years he was locked up in an asylum at Cambridge, Mass, kept by Dock Eliot an' was discharged as oncurable.'

"'No,' says another, 'it ain't lunacy. It's drink. I know it. I have it on the best authority that at a diplomatic dinner he pasted Monseer Jusserand in th' eye because iv a dispute about th' Fr-rinch language.'

"It is well known that th' fam'ly got Bob Bacon to go into th' cabinet because he's a big, strong man an' cud handle him whin he was on wan iv his tanthrums.

"I wud be willin' to go on th' stand an' swear that he was how-com-ye-so wan day whin I see him on a horse jumpin' a fence. Any man that jumps a horse over a fence must be dhrunk.'

"Well, this here honest iditor heerd these stories, an' it was his plain jooty to publish thim, f'r ivry iditor, especially an iditor in Ishpening, has heavy responsibilities in keepin' wicked or intimprate men out iv the White House.

"Besides, it looked like a million to wan that this gr-reat journal iv civilization wud escape th' eye iv th' Jawn B. Gough iv Eyesther Bay.

"So he popped in his cheerful little item, sint th' pa-aper to press, an' wint home an' thought no more about it ontil lo an' behold! Tiddy Rosenfelt, escorted be an army iv witnesses, descinded on him an' sued him f'r libel.

"I read ivry line iv th' tistymony, an' will say this, that there'd be no money f'r me in havin' Tiddy Rosenfelt as a customer aven whin attinded be a physician.

"I run no dairy, Hinnissy, an' th' amount iv milk consumed be this statesman to escoort into his system a couple iv spoonfuls iv brandy wud keep a herd iv cows wurrukin' nights.

"It appears fr'm th' ividince that at times he was compelled to dhrink be a wicked doctor. This here evil inflooence stood at his elbow whin he was weak an' suffrin' an' compelled him to debauch himsilf with wan spoonful afther another iv brandy.

"'I can't do it, dock,' he pleaded. 'Don't ask me to pollute this serene an' beautiful milk with th' accursed stuff.'

"'Dhrink,' says th' inflexible agent iv th' divvle. 'Dhrink or die,' he says.

"'But won't wan spoonful be enough?' begs th' prisidint.

"'No,' says th' dock in a hollow voice. 'Ye must take two.'

"'Thin pull down th' curtains so that me example may not corrupt an innicint wurruld,' says th' gr-reat man, an', writhin' in pain, he consumes th' nauseios mixture, an', flingin th' glass fr'm him, falls onconscious on th' flure.

"All th' witnesses corrobyrated him. It seems fr'm their testymony that durin' th' Rosenfelt administhration a pretty custom prevailed at th' White House called 'Sniffin' f'r booze.'

"Wan iv th' Prisidints intimate frinds wud dhrop in on him iv an afthernoon, an', afther exchangin' th' usual civilities, wud requist th' Prisidint to blow in his face.

"He would thin take out a notebook an' jot down: 'June 5. Still no thrace. Called afther dinner an' made repeated assays. Results mostly nigative, but found indications iv what may be Rhine wine.'

"Hundreds iv witnesses that had subjected His Excellency to this test wint on th' stand an' swore that they'd never got anny results.

" 'Did ye or did ye not,' thundered th' lawyers, 'iver detic alcohol on th' Prisidint's breath?'

" 'Niver, as Hiven is me judge,' declared th' witnesses in ringin' tones.

"Whin it come th' turn iv th' poor iditor man he wasn't able to presint a single witness to prove that Tiddy was a dipsomanyac.

"No, sir; iv all th' people that were ready to take their oath that they'd seen our hayro whin he was fitter f'r an ambulance thin an office, divvle th' wan turned up at his call to go on th' stand.

"So he was obliged to do th' manly thing iv readin' a docymint containin' an' account iv his own noble life, with a few wurruds on th' circylation iv his excellent pa-aper an its value as an advertisin' meejum, an' acknowledgin' that he had tossed off th' lie undher th' imprission that it was th' thruth, because it was in th' heat iv th' campaign an' he didn't expict to be sued, but he was glad he had been, an' there was nawthin' f'r him to do but admit that his witnesses had run out on him an' he cudden't prove annything.

"This handsome apology was accipted, th' jury give a verdict iv six cints damages, th' colonel says, 'A gloryous victhry, be George,' th' iditor sint over an' borrowed th' money fr'm th' foreman, an' th' colonel, attinded be his calvacade iv breath investigators, returned home with th' cash jinglin' in his pockets—vindicated.

"I wondher what it's comin' to? Nex' year I expict to see banners in front iv headquarthers sayin',

'Vote f'r Higgins. His breath is ba'my,' or 'Sullivan an' sody,' or th' like iv that.

"Will it come about that whin an orator gets up to advycate a candydate he'll be compilled to say whether he has or has not made a personal invistigation iv th' candydate's exhalations?

"Will a comity be called befure th' convintion to report that they have made a searchin' inquiry into th' candydate's breath f'r two months, an' without goin' into other details they are prepared to say that it has showed no signs iv alcohol?

"If so, Hinnissy, I'm goin' out iv pollyticks an' into dentisthry.

"But what I can't undherstand, Hinnissy, is why if this here shellac that beams down on us fr'm th' shelves is so bad to take, th' governmint shud go into partnership with thim that sells it. Here's me frind Dock Wilson an' me frind Willum McAdoo an' me frind Willum Jennings Bryan settin together discussin' th' repoort iv th' sicrety iv th' treasury.

" 'Mack,' says th' prisidint, "I hope ye don't dhrink.'

" 'I sincerely hope so, too,' says th' sicrety iv state.

" 'I dhrink very little,' says th' sicrety iv th' treasury.

" 'Don't do it at all,' says th' prisidint. It's a turrble habit. Dhrink is th' curse iv modhren civilyzation. It fills our citizens an' it fills our jails an' our pinitinchries, our insane asylums an' our wurruk houses with our citizens. Stop it now.

" 'Ye say ye had on'y wan glass iv claret at dinner? It is wan too manny. Remimber th' rapids ar-re below. We will now take up th' financyal repoort," he says.

" 'Well,' says th' sicrety iv th' threasury, 'to begin with I'm glad to tell ye that th' intarnal rivnoo receipts f'r th' comin' year will be about a millyon dollars more thin they were last year. I base these figures on th' increasin' thirst iv our people.'

" 'How splindid,' says th' prisidint. 'I mane how tur-rble. How tur-rbly splindid. It manes much to th' administration,' he says.

" 'This is good news indeed,' says Willum Jennings Bryan."

"An' there ye ar-re. I can't make it out, but there's lots iv things in th' wurruld that I can't make out.

"I suppose th' Government is like mesilf. No wan is more iv a timp'rance advycate thin I am, f'r I've expeeryance. If ye think 'tis a pleasure f'r me to stand here ladlin' out this household ammony an' listenin' to th' harsh sounds it causes ye to mistake f'r convarsation ye don't know me.

"If I had me way an' didn't love th' beautiful sthream on whose banks I've lived these manny years I'd take all th' stuff in thim bottles an' poor thim into th' Chicago River. I wud so.

"I don't undherstand how anny wan pays me f'r it. It wud be just as raisonable f'r ye to say: 'Here take $2 an' hit me over th' head with th' bung starter.' It be more so, f'r in that case ye wudden't come back f'r more.

But what am I to do? I s'pose th' Govermint an'

meself ar-re in th' same box. We both have to be
supported, an' this is th' only way we know. An'
it's a pretty good sign that th' people ar-re slowin'
down on th' stuff whin our statesmin ar-re askin'
all th' wurruld to step up an' have a smell.

"For a statesman, Hinnissy, is a fellow that finds
out which way th' procissyon is goin' an' thin runs
out an' grabs th' stick fr'm th' dhrum major."

"Ye don't think T.R. iver dhrank too much, do
ye?" asked Mr. Hennessey.

"I've been a student as well as an insthructor iv
th' dhrink habit f'r manny years," said Mr. Dooley,
an' I'll tell you this. I know fr'm obsarvation that
"no ardent collictor iv specimens iv rum can keep on
goin' fast.

"He can go fast, sometimes, but he can't go far
an' go fast. At best he's a quarther horse, an' of-
times whin he thinks he's gone a mile he's ra-aly
been left at th' post."

On the Recall of Judges

"Ar-re ye in favor iv th' in-th' what-d'ye-call-it-
an' th' r'firindum an' th' recall?" asked Mr. Hennessy.

"Am I in favor iv what?" said Mr. Dooley.

"Iv th' init- th' in-" Mr. Hennessy tried again.

"Niver mind tellin' me," Mr. Dooley interrupted.
"I know what ye mean be th' faces ye're makin'. No,
I'm not. I'm not in favor iv ayether iv these gloryous principals that has been handed down to us fr'm
our Swiss ancesthors. Man an' boy I've voted f'r

fifty years f'r pollytickal issues that I cudden't undherstand, but I dhraw the line whin they hand me
issues that I can't aven pronounce. I've been a free
thrader, although ivrything I read proved to me if
I got me foolish wishes I'd be rooned through th'
products iv th' pauper labor iv Europe poorin' in an'
floodin' ye out iv ye'er job.

"That bribe of two twinty-five a day that ye ca-
jole out iv th' steel thrust f'r takin' a healthy
amount iv exercise wud go, an' whin it wint, down
wud fall this splindid commercial intherprise that
I've built up. So I voted f'r free thrade. An' me frind
Silo, th' thruck farmer, who knew he was bein'
crushed be th' tariff, voted to go on bein' crushed.
It was all right. If he won th' tariff stayed an' if I
won it was increased, an there we were with nawthin' to throuble us between illictions.

"But these new issues ar-re diff'rent. Suppose I
say I'm f'r thim. 'Ar're ye f'r th'—as ye said—an' th'
so-an'-so?' says th' judge iv illiction. 'I am,' says I
in a ringin' voice. 'I wud die f'r thim,' says I. 'Thin
spell thim,' says th' judge iv illiction. An' I faint with
shame.

"But th' recall is betther. I can pronounce that
without prematurely agein' me face. Besides 'tis a
fine issue. Ye don't have to get a college pro-fissor
to take a pointer an' a diagram an' explain it to th'
other ign'rant voters. They know all about it.
They've been votin' f'r it f'r years. Put in simple
language it is: 'We're tired iv him. Throw him out.'
Nawthin' is more raisonable thin that an' nawthin'

will go home quicker to th' gin'rous heart iv th' people iv this gr-reat counthry. Supposin' some fellow goes to th' legislachure as a frind iv th' people an' th' on'y wan iv his old chums that can get to see him a month afther he's at th' capitol is th' janyal prisidint iv th' gas comp'ny.

Well, wan day ye see his wife go by in an autymobill an' ye say: 'Don't ye think Higgins has got enough? Let's put th' law on him.' So we go down to Springfield an' we say: 'Bill, ye're such a good fellow that we can't do without ye. We miss ye're smilin' face on th' scow. Ye must be with us again. An' to show ye how kind we feel to'rds ye we've found ye're old pick an' shovel an' brought thim to ye.' An' wan iv us takes him be th' hair an' th' other be th' heels an' we throw him out iv the window. An' that's th' recall.

"It suits me th' best iv all th' issues iv th' year. There's nowhere I hate to see th' same old face thin whith its feet up on th' desk iv a pollytickal office. An' they ain't anny rule iv life betther thin this, that whin ye put a man on a perch an' he don't sing th' way ye want, bump him off.

"Am I in favor iv recallin' th' judges, too? Ye bet I am. Well, maybe I wudden't recall thim exactly. A judge that's been on th' bench anny lenth iv time is poor comp'ny in a crowd. If he says, 'It's a fine day,' an ye say 'It ain't,' he's apt to think he's still on the bench an' hand ye a punch. Whin a man gets what Hogan calls th' judicyal timper it means he's cross all th' time. So p'rhaps I wudden't haul thim

back to publick life. But I'd pretind I was goin' to.
Ivry wanst in a while I'd give thim a dark look, as
much as to say: 'An' I'll get ye, too, me good fellow,
if ye don't brace up. An' I'm th' boy that can do it.'
An' afther a while whin I said 'How d'ye do?' to him
he might say somethin' more janyal thin 'Thirty
days.'

"Ye see, tis this way. Ye mind little Levy that
was illiction judge. He was th' junyor mimber iv
th' firm iv lawyers that done al th' legal wurruk in
th' common council f'r Garrity, th' big conthractor.
I guess he wasn't much good in th' office, so Perk-
ins, his boss, made a judge iv him. He was a pleasant man durin' th' campaign, an' there was a frind
iv mine that wint crazy about him.

"His name was Dougherty. Dougherty cudden't
say too much about his frind Judge Levy. He begun
callin' him Judge two months befure th' illiction.
'There's a man that'll make a mark f'r himself,' says
he. 'He's got th' fine constitutional mind,' he says.
'An' a pleasant man an' a frind iv th' poor an' down-
throdden,' he says. Well, Dougherty illicted him, or
annyhow thought he did, an' th' judge leaped upon
th' bench. I guess he made a good judge. Whin he
sint a man down th' road f'r forty or fifty years he
always give him such a dhressin' down that th' pris'-
ner was glad to get away where he'd be safe. His
interpretations iv th' constitution was gr-rand. 'Tis
funny about th' constitution. It reads plain, but no
wan can undherstant it without an' interpreter. This
here frind iv Dougherty's thranslated th' ol' consti-

tution into Yiddish, low German, Fr-rinch, Roosh-yan, an arly English.

"Annyhow, it was Dougherty's good luck to have a case befure him. If I iver go into coort th' polis'll have to take me in chains. I'm a gr-reat reader, an', as Hogan says, familyarity with decisions breeds contimpt iv coort. But Dougherty didn't know, an' whin he'd stepped into a hole in th' flure at th' factory an' broke his leg he got a lawyer an' sued Flannigan, th' owner. Th' lawyer told Dougherty that th' laste Flannigan wud have to do to square himsilf was to give him th' facthry an' a pair iv goold crutches to hop to an' fr'm his autymobill on. Dougherty got so proud over this here sudden flood iv wealth that there was no talkin' to him. If ye ast him what he was doin' he wud say, 'Lookin' afther me lawsuit,' as much to say, 'Runnin' me bank.'

"Well, sir, th' case come to thrile an' Dougherty wint to th' coorthouse. He thought his old frind seemed near sighted, f'r whin Dougherty thried to wave his hankerchief at him his honor motioned to th' coort attendant. Durin' th' examination this binivolent monarch dhrew pitchers on a pa-aper, but he showed two or three times that he remimbered Dougherty be sayin', 'Speak up, me man,' or 'Answer th' question or I'll lock ye up.'

"Fin'lly whin all th' evidence was in th' judge motioned th' coort polisman to throw Dougherty out, an' thin spoke as follows: 'This here case started Dougherty again Flannigan, but it's now me again congress, an' I give th' verdick f'r mesilf, an' if I had

congress here I'd sind it to jail f'r passin' a law in
favor iv this here polthroon. I've half a mind now
to ordher me bailiff to pinch th' house iv reprinsinta-
tives, th' sinit, an' th' prisidint that signed th' law
an' put thim in th' basteel.' 'Th' constitution says
they had a right to,' says Dougherty's lawyer.
'Eighty days f'r contimpt iv coort,' says his honor.
'If th' constitution says so it niver meant it. What
did the constitution say? I don't know, but undher
th' decision iv Lord Justice Poke in th' Eighth Eliza-
beth, a man in Dougherty's job was th' same as a
horse an' he can't've changed. Who iver heerd iv a
horse collictin' damages? It wud be conthry to all
th' rules iv law an' property,' says he. 'D'ye mean
to say I'm th' same as a horse? says Dougherty.
'That is ye'er status,' says the coort. 'Thin, says
Dougherty, 'if I've got a broken leg Flannigan has
a right to shoot me an' I'd betther be goin', an' he
broke another leg on th' stairs but he sued th' county
and received damages.

"Don't I think a poor man has a chanst in coort?
Iv coorse he has. He has th' same chanst there that
he has outside. He has a splendid, poor man's chanst.
Annhow, he ought to stay out iv coort onless he's
done somethin' pleasant to get himsilf there. It's no
place f'r him or f'r anny man, rich or poor, to go
fortune huntin.'

"An' do I think th' judges'll iver be recalled? Faith,
I do not. Wud ye lave anny wan recall me if ye was
a judge. I see mesilf doin' it. Whin th' popylace
thried to whistle me back to practice law on th' third

flure I'd call th' bailiff over an' say: 'James, get out
th' handcuffs.'

"Ye can bet that th' first law recallin' th' judges
will be pronounced onconstitutional be th' entire
joodicyary iv th' counthry be a risin' vote an' with
three hearty cheers. If I was a judge I wud know
that a law throwin' me out iv a job was onconstitutional at wanst, ex post facto, ex propria vigore, an'
de juribus non dispytandum, as Hogan says. An' I
wudden't have to get th' constitution out iv th' safe
to decide it ayether. I'd decide it accordin to me grocery bill.

"No, sir, ye'll live a long time befure ye iver see
judges recalled. But it don't do anny harm to scare
thim. It don't do annyway anny harm to scare thim
wanst in a while. They've f'rgotten we're outside.
We'll make a noise, an' whin they say, 'Ar're they
goin' to haul me out?' We'll yell, 'Judge, put ye'er
head out iv th' window. There ar-re people out here.
That's it—people, not lawyers. We don't objick to
ye'er makin' laws, but don't make thim on'y f'r lawyers. Cut out a few pattherns that will fit us, too.
We don't want manny, but we'd like a few simple
wans that we can wear to keep off th' cold. An' if ye
haven't time f'r annything excipt a harness that we
ar-re not iddycated enough to put on, f'r hivens sake
let us make some laws f'r ourselves that plazes our
low tastes. We don't want laws to wear in coort. We
want thim to wear outside.

"What is this English common law I read about?"
asked Mr. Hennessy.

"It's th' law I left Ireland to get away fr'm," said Mr. Dooley. "If it's pursooed me over here I'll go to Chiny."

Reform Administration

"Why is it," asked Mr. Hennessy, "that a rayform administhration always goes to th' bad?"

"I'll tell ye," said Mr. Dooley. "I tell ye ivrything an' I'll tell ye this. In th' first place 'tis a gr-reat mistake to think that annywan ra-aly wants to rayform. Ye niver heerd iv a man rayformin' himsilf. He'll rayform other people gladly. He likes to do it. But a healthy man'll niver rayform while he has th' strenth. A man doesn't rayform till his will has been impaired so he hasn't power to resist what th' pa-apers calls th' blandishments iv th' timpter. An' that's thruer in politics thin annywhere else.

"But a rayformer don't see it. A rayformer thinks he was ilicted because he was a rayformer, whin th' thruth iv th' matther is he was ilicted because no wan knew him. Ye can always ilict a man in this counthry on that platform. If I was runnin' f'r office, I'd change me name, an' have printed on me cards: 'Give him a chanst; he can't be worse.' He's ilicted because th' people don't know him an' do know th' other la-ad; because Mrs. Casey's oldest boy was clubbed be a polisman, because we cudden't get wather above th' third story wan day, because th' sthreet car didn't stop f'r us, because th' Flannigans bought a pianny, because we was near run over be a mail wagon, because th' saloons are open

Sunday night, because they're not open all day, an' because we're tired seein' th' same face at th' window whin we go down to pay th' wather taxes. Th' rayformer don't know this. He thinks you an' me, Hinnissy, has been watchin' his spotless career f'r twinty years, that we've read all he had to say on th' evils iv pop'lar sufferage befure th' Society f'r the Bewildermint iv th' Poor, an' that we're achin' in ivry joint to have him dhrag us be th' hair iv th' head fr'm th' flowin' bowl an' th' short card game, make good citizens iv us an' sind us to th' pinitinchry. So th' minyit he gets into th' job he begins a furyous attimpt to convart us into what we've been thryin' not to be iver since we come into th' wurruld.

"In th' coorse iv th' twinty years that he spint attimptin' to get office, he managed to poke a few warrum laws conthrollin' th' pleasures iv th' poor into th' stachoo book, because no wan cared about thim or because they made business betther f'r th' polis, an' whin he's in office, he calls up th' Cap'n iv the polis an' says he: 'If these laws ar-re bad laws th' way to end thim is to enfoorce thim.' Somebody told him that, Hinnissy. It isn't thrue, d'ye mind. I don't care who said it, not if 'twas Willum Shakespere. It isn't thrue. Laws ar-re made to throuble people an' th' more throuble they make th' longer they stay on th' stachoo book. But th' polis don't ast anny questions. Says they: 'They'll be less money in th' job but we need some recreation,' an' that night a big copper comes down th' sthreet, sees me settin' out on th' front stoop with me countenance dhraped with a tin pail, fans me with his club an' runs me in. Th' woman nex' dure is locked up f'r sthringin' a clothes line on th' roof, Hannigan's boy Tim gets tin days f'r keepin a goat, th' polis resarves are called out to protict th' vested rights iv property against th' haynyous pushcart man, th' stations is crowded with felons charged with maintainin' a hose conthrary to th' stachoos made an' provided, an' th' tindherline is all over town. A rayformer don't think annything has been accomplished if they'se a vacant bedroom in th' pinitinchry. His motto is 'Arrest that man.'

"Whin a rayformer is ilicted he promises ye a business administhration. Some people want that but I don't. Th' American business man is too fly. He's all right, d'ye mind. I don't say annything again' him. He is what Hogan calls th' boolwarks iv progress, an' we cudden't get on without him even if his scales are a little too quick to th' dhrop. But he ought to be left to dale with his akels. 'Tis a shame to give him a place where he can put th' comether on millions iv people that has had no business thrainin' beyond occasionally handin' a piece iv debased money to a car conductor on a cold day. A reg'lar pollytician can't give away an alley without blushin', but a business man who is in pollytics jus' to see that th' civil sarvice law gets thurly enfoorced, will give Lincoln Park an' th' public libr'y to th' beef thrust, charge an admission price to th' lake front an' make it a felony f'r annywan to buy stove polish outside iv his store, an' have it all put down to public improvemints with a pitcher iv him in th' corner stone.

"Fortchnitly, Hinnissy, a rayformer is seldom a business man. He thinks he is, but business men know diff'rent. They know what he is. He thinks business an' honesty is th' same thing. He does, indeed. He's got thim mixed because they dhress alike. His idee is that all he has to do to make a business administhration is to have honest men ar-round him. Wrong. I'm not sayin', mind ye, that a man can't do good work an' be honest at th' same time. But whin I'm hirin' a la-ad I find out first whether he is onto his job, an' afther a few years I begin to suspect that he is honest, too. Manny a dishonest man can lay brick sthraight an' manny a man that wudden't steal ye'er spoons will break ye'er furniture. I don't want Father Kelly to hear me, but I'd rather have a competint man who wud steal if I give him a chanst, but I won't, do me plumbin' thin a person that wud scorn to help himsilf but didn't know how to wipe a joint. Ivry man ought to be honest to start with, but to give a man an office jus' because he's honest is like ilictin' him to Congress because he's a pathrite, because he don't bate his wife or because he always wears a right boot on th' right foot. A man ought to be honest to start with an' afther that he ought to be crafty. A pollytician who's on'y honest is jus' th' same as bein' out in a winther storm without anny clothes on.

"Another thing about rayform administhrations is they always think th' on'y man that ought to hold a job is a lawyer. Th' raison is that in th' coorse iv his thrainin' a lawyer larns enough about ivrything to make a good front on anny subject to annybody who doesn't know about it. So whin th' rayform administhration comes in th' mayor says: 'Who'll we make chief iv polis in place iv th' misguided ruffyan who has held th' job f'r twinty years?' 'Th' man f'r th' place,' says th' mayor's adviser, 'is Arthur Lightout,' he says. 'He's an ixcillent lawyer, Yale, '95, an' is well up on polis matthers. Las' year he read a paper on "The fine polis foorce iv London" befure th' annyal meetin' iv th' S'ciety f'r Ladin' th' Mulligan Fam'ly to a Betther an' Harder Life. Besides,' he says, 'he's been in th' milishy an' th' foorce needs a man who'll be afraid not to shoot in case iv public disturbance.' So Arthur takes hold iv th' constabulary an' in a year th' polis can all read Emerson an' th' burglars begin puttin' up laddhers an' block an' tackles befure eight A.M. An' so it is on ivry side. A lawyer has charge iv the city horse-shoein', another wan is clainin' th' sthreets, th' author iv 'Gasamagoo on torts' is thryin' to dispose iv th' ashes be throwin' thim in th' air on a windy day, an' th' bright boy that took th' silver ware f'r th' essay on ne exeats an' their relation to life is plannin' a uniform that will be sarviceable an' constitchoochinal f'r th' brave men that wurruks on th' city dumps. An' wan day th' main rayformer goes out expictin' to rayccive th' thanks iv th' community an' th' public that has jus' got out iv jail f'r lettin' th' wather run too long in th' bath tub rises up an' cries:

'Back to th' Univarsity Settlemint.' Th' man with th' di'mon' in his shirt front comes home an' pushes th' honest lawyers down th' steps, an' a dishonest horse shoer shoes th' city's horses well, an' a crooked plumber does th' city's plumbin' securely, an' a rascally polisman that may not be avarse to pickin' up a bet but will always find out whin Pathrolman Scanlan slept on his beat, takes hold iv th' polis foorce, an' we raysume our nachral condition iv illagal merrimint. An' th' rayformer spinds th' rest iv his life tellin' us where we are wrong. He's good at that. On'y he don't undherstand that people wud rather be wrong an' comfortable thin right in jail."

"I don't like a rayformer," said Mr. Hennessy.

"Or anny other raypublican," said Mr. Dooley.

Platform Making

That sthrikes me as a gran' platform," said Mr. Hennessy. "I'm with it fr'm start to finish."

"Sure ye are," said Mr. Dooley, "an' so ye'd be if it begun: 'We denounce Terence Hinnissy iv th' Sixth Ward iv Chicago as a thraitor to his country, an inimy iv civilization, an' a poor thing.' Ye'd say: 'While there are wan or two things that might be omitted, th' platform as a whole is a statesmanlike docymint, an' wan that appeals to th' intelligince iv American manhood.' That's what ye'd say, an' that's what all th' likes iv ye'd say. An' whin iliction day comes 'round th' on'y question ye'll ast ye'ersilf is: 'Am I with Mack or am I with Billy Bryan?' An accordin'ly ye'll vote.

" 'Tis always th' same way, an' all platforms is alike. I mind wanst whin I was an alter-nate to th' county con-vintion—'twas whin I was a power in pollytics an' th' on'y man that cud do annything with th' Bohemian vote—I was settin' here wan night with a pen an' a pot iv ink befure me, thryin' to compose th' platform f'r th' nex' day, f'r I was a lithry man in a way, d'ye mind, an' I knew th' la-ads'd want a few crimps put in th' raypublicans in a ginteel style, an' 'd be sure to call on me f'r to do it. Well, I'd got as far down as th' tariff an' was thryin' f'r to express me opinyon without swearin', whin who shud come in but Lafferty, that was sicrety iv McMahon, that was th' Main Guy in thim days, but aftherward thrun down on account iv him mixin' up between th' Rorkes an' th' Dorseys. Th' Main Guy Down Town said he wudden't have no throuble in th' ward, an' he de-clared McMahon out. McMahon had too much money annyhow. If he'd kept on, dollar bills'd have been extinct outside iv his house. But he was a sthrong man in thim days an' much liked.

"Anyhow, Lafferty, that was his sicrety, come in, an' says he: 'What are ye doin' there?' says he. 'Step soft,' says I; 'I am at wurruk,' I says. 'Ye shudden't do lithry wurruk on an empty stomach,' says he. 'I do nawthin' on an empty stomach but eat,' says I. 'I've had me supper,' I says. 'Go 'way,' says I, 'till I finish th' platform,' I says. 'What's th' platform?' says he. 'F'r th' county con-vintion,' says I.

"Well, sir, he set down on a chair, an' I thought th' man was goin' to die right there on the premises with laughter. 'Whin ye get through with ye'er barkin',' says I, 'I'll throuble ye to tell me what ye may be doin' it f'r,' I says. 'I see nawthin' amusin' here but ye'er prisince,' I says, 'an' that's not a div-vle iv a lot funnier than a wooden leg,' I says, f'r I was mad. Afther awhile he come to, an' says he: 'Ye don't raally think,' says he, 'that ye'll get a chanct to spring that platform,' he says. 'I do,' says I. 'Why,' he says, 'the platform has been adopted,' he says. 'Whin?' says I. 'Befure ye were born,' says he. 'In th' reign iv Bildad th' first,' says he—he was a larned man, was Lafferty, though a dhrinkin' man. All sicreties iv pollyticians not in office is drhinkin' men, Hinnissy. 'Ive got th' copy iv it here in me pocket,' he says. 'Th' boss give it to me to bring it up to date,' he says. 'They was no sthrike last year an' we've got to put a sthrike plank in th' platform or put th' prisident iv th' Lum-ber Shovers' union on th' county board, an',' he says, 'they ain't room,' he says.

" 'Why,' says Lafferty, 'ye ought to know th' his-thry iv platforms,' he says. An' he give it to me, an' I'll give it to ye. Years ago, Hinnissy, manny years ago, they was a race between th' dimmycrats an' th' raypublicans f'r to see which shud have a choice iv principles. Th' dimmycrats lost. I dinnaw why. Mebbe they stopped to take a dhrink. Annyhow, they lost. Th' raypublicans come up an' they choose th' 'we commind' principles, an' they was nawthin' left f'r the dimmycrats but th' 'we denounce an' deplores.' I dinnaw how it come about, but th' dimmycrats didn't like th' way th' thing shtud, an' so they fixed it up between thim that whichiver won at th' iliction shud commind an' congratulate, an' thim that lost shud denounce an' deplore. An' so it's been, on'y the dimmycrats has had so little chanct f'r to do annything but denounce an' deplore that they've almost lost th' use iv th' other wurruds.

"Mack sets back in Wash'nton an' writes a platform f'r th' comity on risolutions to compose th' week afther. He's got a good job—forty-nine ninety-two, sixty-six a month—an' 'tis up to him to feel good. 'I—I mean we,' he says, 'congratulate th' counthry on th' matchless statesmanship, onshrinkin' courage, steady devotion to duty an' principle iv that gallant an' hon'rable leader, mesilf,' he says to his sicrety. 'Take that,' he says, 'an' elaborate it,' he says. 'Ye'll find a ditchnry on th' shelf near the dure,' he says, 'if ye don't think I've put what I give ye sthrong enough,' he says. 'I always was,' he says, 'too retirin' f'r me own good,' he says. 'Spin out th' r-rest,' he says, 'to make about six thousan' wurruds,' he says, 'but be sure don't write annything too hot about th' Boer war or th' Ph'lippeens or Chiny, or th' tariff, or th' goold question, or our relations with England, or th' civil sarvice,' he says. 'Tis a foolish man,' he says, 'that throws a hunk iv coal fr'm his own window at th' dhriver iv a brick wagon,' he says.

"But with Billy Bryan 'tis diff'rent. He's out in

Lincoln, Neebrasky, far fr'm home, an' he says to himsilf: 'Me throat is hoarse, an' I'll exercise me other fac'lties,' he says. 'I'll write a platform,' he says. An' he sets down to a typewriter, an' denounces an' deplores till th' hired man blows th' dinner horn. Whin he can denounce an' deplore no longer he views with alarm an' declares with indignation. An' he sinds it down to Kansas City, where th' cot beds come fr'm."

"Oh, ye're always pitchin' into some wan," said Mr. Hennessy. "I bet ye Willum Jennings Bryan niver see th' platform befure it wint in. He's too good a man."

"He is all iv that," said Mr. Dooley. "But ye bet he knows th' rale platform f'r him is: 'Look at th' bad breaks Mack's made,' an' Mack's platform is: 'Ye'd get worse if ye had Billy Bryan.' An' it depinds on whether most iv th' voters ar-re tired out or on'y a little tired who's ilicted. All excipt you, Hinnissy. Ye'll vote f'r Bryan?"

"I will," said Mr. Hennessy.

"Well," said Mr. Dooley, "d'ye know, I suspicted ye might."

RELAXATION

A YACHT CLUB, SAYS MR. DOOLEY, IS AN ASSOCIATION OF LAWYERS.

On Making a Will

"I niver made a will," said Mr. Dooley. "I didn't want to give mesilf a headache thinkin' iv something to put into it.

"A will iv mine wud be a funny little thing, anyhow, an' if anywan thried to file it he'd be li-ble to be locked up f'r contimpt iv th' Probate Coort.

"Besides, I wudden't like to cause anny onseemly wrangles, an' maybe lawsuits, among me heirs about who wud pay f'r th' express wagon to carry th' estate to th' city dump.

"An' anyhow I've always thought that if there's goin' to be ayether cheers or tears at me obsekeez they should spring fr'm th' heart, not fr'm mercinary motives.

"If any fellow feels like cillybratin' me departure let him do it out iv his own pocket. Thin I'll know he's sincere. 'Twud grieve me if somewan broke into song at th' news an' a sthranger was to ask, 'Is that wan iv his inimies?' an' th' reply wud be 'No, it's wan iv his heirs.'

"So f'r wan reason or another I've niver made a will, but I'll not deny it must be considhrable spoort f'r thim that has th' manes an' th' imagination to injye it.

"I'm pretty sure I'd break into tears whin th' law-

yers wrote down th' directions f'r somebody else to
set in me rockin' chair, an' I can't think iv annything
that wud brighten th' wurruld with me out iv it. But
that wud be because I wudden't go at it in th' right
way.

"To be injyeable a will must be at wan an' th' same
time a practical joke on th' heirs an' an advertisement iv th' ol' crust that made it.

"Many a man niver has his own way till he has it
through his will. Afther he's dead an' gone, he
shoves his hat on th' back iv his head an' stalks up
an' down through th' house sayin', 'I'll show ye who's
th' boss here. F'r th' first time in me life now that
I'm dead, I'm goin' to be obeyed.'

"No wondher that manny meek millyonaires comforts their declinin' years with this amusement. It
is, as Hogan says, th' last infirmary f'r their noble
minds.

"It's a chance f'r thim to tache th' fam'ly their
proper place an' blow their own horns without havin' anywan intherrupt th' solo.

"I was readin' a fine will th' other day. I niver see
th' la-ad that made it, but I can think iv him walkin'
up an' down th' lawyers office as he dictated it,
whackin' himself on th' chest an' sayin', 'Bedad'
afther ivry paragraph.

"It wint something like this: 'I, Ephraim Snivvy,
bein' iv a sound mind, no matther what may come
out in coort later, but ralizin' that th' repytation iv
me onparelleled succiss in business has spread so

far that I am li'able to be called elsewhere, do make this me last will an' testymint.

" 'All me money I lave to me faithful frind th' Confidintyal Chattel Morgedge Comp'ny, which I command to disburse as follows:

" 'To me devoted wife, Frances Ethil Snivvy, shall be paid th' sum iv four hundherd dollars per annum, undher th' followin' conditions: That she shall niver marry again; that she shall wear a black veil f'r th' rest iv her life in me honor; that she shall go to me grave wanst a week an' bedew it with her tears; that she shall be sorry that she often spoke to me th' way she did; that she shall wear suspinded fr'm her neck a photygraft iv me framed in rhinestones; that she shall keep th' ile paintin' iv me in th' parlor in good repair; that she shall not attind anny dance, bankit, theaytre, wake or other frivolous intertainmint. If she fails to comply with anny iv these conditions, or if anny man undher th' age iv eighty is discovered in her neighborhood, or if she is iver seen to laugh in public, I direct me exicutors to cut her off fr'm me bounty an' turn her out on th' wurruld f'r th' heartless flirt she is.

" 'To me son David I lave th' use iv me horse an' buggy an' two bags iv oats ontil he has arrived at th' age iv forty-five. If at that time he has showed a proper apprecyation iv th' thrust, th' said property shall pass to his ownership undher condition that me name shall appear in letters a foot high on th' dashboord.

" 'Me sicond son Steven I have provided f'r already be lettin' him get himsilf a good job in a blacksmith shop.

" 'Me son Elias, havin' offinded me be goin' to a baseball game, I desire that he shall get nawthin fr'm me estate.

" 'To me daughter Eliza I lave th' kitchen range in thrust. In this age iv fortune hunters a father cannot be too careful, hince I direct that she shall not marry ontil she arrives at th' age iv fifty. At that time, if she sees fit to bestow her hand on a worthy young man who shall be acciptable to th' loan comity iv me bank, I direct that she shall be paid three dollars a week out iv her mother's allowance, th' said fund to be known as 'Th' Gin'rous ol' Eph Snivvy Foundation f'r Indygint Daughters.''

" 'To me faithful frind an' nurse, Bedalia O'Brien, who has survd me devotedly f'r twinty years, an' who is now too old f'r other injyemint I lave me collection iv old medicine bottles.

" 'To Willum Waldorf Astor I lave me straw hat on condition that he changes his name to Snivvy.

" 'To th' mayor in Venice, Italy, I lave two dollars to erect a monymint to me an' alter th' name iv th' town to Snivvyville.

" 'Th' rest an' residoo iv me splindid fortune I lave in thrust to me on'y frind th' Confidintyal Chattel Morgedge Bank an' direct thim to let it accumylate ontil it amounts to four million dollars. This sum they will expind in erectin' a chimbley in white marble an' goold on th' Snivvy Glue Wurruks, said chimbley to be at laste thirty feet higher thin any in th' neighborhood with an electhric sign which shall be kept constantly burnin' with th' motto, "Snivvy, he done it."

"Yes, sir, it must be fun makin' a will. Think iv th' throuble ye can cause an' th' insults ye can hurl at ye'er enimies. I often thought 'twud be a fine way iv gettin' even with a man I didn't like.

"Supposin' Hogan an' me had a quarrel, an' I didn't have time to write a frindly bi-ography about him, or was afraid I might go first, nawthin' wud be nater thin to put him in me will. 'I hereby cancel all bequests to me frind Abdul Hogan on account iv his bad habits.' I bet he'd be sorry I was gone. How he'd wish he cud have me back again f'r awhile.

"I niver see anywan that enthered into th' spirit iv makin' a will so thurly as our ol' frind Dochney. Ye didn't like him, but I did. I liked him because he was so simple an' sincere.

"Prudent fellows like yirsilf, that spind ye'er lives pilin' up great stores iv good will an' affiction an' a comfortable conscience f'r ye'er old age, don't apprecyate a spindthrift like Dochney, who threw all these things away in th' pursuit iv his pleasure, which was makin' money.

"Ye thought he was a bad man, but I knew him f'r a single-minded, innocint ol' la-ad, who niver harmed anywan excipt f'r gain, an' was incapable iv falsehood outside iv business.

"To those who see him in th' rough battle in life at home or among his neighbors, he may've seemed hard, but we who knew him in th' quiet seclusyon iv

th' bank among his recreations, found another Dochney, a cheerful soul, who always had a smile on his
face, who set little verses to th' promissory notes an'
cudden't keep his feet still whin th' goold coin clat-
tered on th' counter.

"If Dochney had wan fault it was he was too sin-
timintal about money. Men like ye ar-re th' re-aly
rapacyous wans. Ye have nawthin' but desire f'r
money. Ye don't want to give it a home an' take care
iv it.

"But Dochney had a tender feelin' f'r it. Tears
come to his eyes as he watched it grow. He became
so attached to it that no wan cud pry it away fr'm
him. An' th' money reciprocated, Ivry dollar he had
wurruked f'r him. It wint out an' decoyed another
dollar, an' aven if it comes back leadin' nawthin'
more thin a little chicken-feed, Dochney wasn't
cross about it.

"He wud pat a nickel on th' back an' say, 'Ye'er
small now, but with a little encouragemint we'll
make a big strappin' dollar out iv ye yit.'

"Dochney lived to an old age because, as th' poet
says, there's nawthin' like avarice to keep a man
young. Th' Spanyards knew that, whin they
marched f'r th' fountain iv perpetchool youth.
They'd heerd th' Indyans had money. Annyhow,
Dochney's cheeks wore th' bloom iv usury long after
many philanthropists ar-re lookin' pale.

"But th' time come whin something in th' eyes iv
his financial frinds told him 'twud be betther not to
go down town again unarmed an' he retired. He

planted his money th' way they do eyesthers an' let
it breed, sindin' down wanst a week to haul out
enough to sustain life an' puttin' th' rest back in
again.

"But this was no life f'r wan that had been an
eyesther pirate in his day, an' Dochney begun to
pine. I thried to amuse him. I had th' Congressman
sind him ivry hour th' new currency bill; I cut out
th' repoorts wanst a week iv th' bankruptcies iv th'
United States an' Canady; I wurruked th' cash reg-
ister f'r him be th' hour because he like th' old re-
frain.

"But nawthin' did him anny good ontil Dock
O'Leary advised him to alter his will. Th' Dock says
he always thries this prescription on aged millyon-
airs afther th' oxygen fails.

"Wan mornin' Dochney come in lookin' as cheerful as an advertisemint iv a breakfast food, an' jinglin' his key ring in his pocket, f'r he niver carrid
annything else to jingle, but made a practice iv ex-
thractin' car fare out iv th' grandchildhers' bank
with a penknife ivry mornin'.

"Ye're lookin' well me ol' buccaneer," said I.

" 'It's feelin' well I am,' says he, fillin' his pocket
from th' cheese bowl. 'I've been with me lawyer all
mornin' revisin' me will. I find I've left out a good
manny ol' frinds. Ye haven't a middle inityal to ye'er
name, have ye?' That's what I told him. 'Give me a
glass iv sasprilly,' he says.

"Well, sir, though I knew th' crafty ol' pirate, th'
thought suddenly lept into me head that maybe his

heart or his brain had softened an' he'd put me in th' will. In that fatal sicond I bought two autymobiles, a yacht, an' a goold watch an' chain, an' shook me ol' frinds. An' whin I come to me sinses he was gone an' hadn't settled f'r th' sasprilly.

"Well, th' fun he had afther that! All day long he wint around makin' delicate inquiries about people's circumstances an' in th' mornin' he was down town puttin' something new in his will.

"He hadn't been a popular man. He had cashed in th' affictions iv his neighbors arly in life. An' prejudices ar-re hard to overcome. But gradually, that is to say, within' a week or ten days, people begun to see that a gr-reat injustice had been done to him.

"He didn't say anything about a will. But he had a way in askin' people did they spell their name with an aitch or a zee an' puttin' it down in a note book that was very consoling. His rilitives begun to show a gr-reat inthrest in him an' some iv thim come fr'm as far as San Francisco to cheer his declinin' years an' form vigilance committees to protect him fr'm fortune-hunters. He was niver alone but always had th' most agreeable society. Twas: 'Uncle, that's a fine cough ye have. Wudden't ye like to set in this cool draft?' Or, 'Cousin Andhrew, tell us that joke ye made las' night. I nearly died laughin' at it, but no wan can tell it like ye'ersilf.'

"He niver took a meal at home. He stopped payin' all bills. He insisted on all babies born in th' ward bein' named afther him. He insulted people an' challenged thim to fight.

"By an' by th' pa-apers got hold iv him an' always spoke iv him as th' eccenthric philanthropist. Rows iv carredges shtud at his dure an' inside in his house he debated with th' thrustees iv binivalint institutions an' prisidints in colledges about their plans f'r new buildings. Wan iv th' ladin' univarsities sint th' glee club down to serenade him. He was ilicted vice prisidint in Andhrew Carnaygie's Peace Committee, thrustee in th' art museum, director in th' Home f'r Wan eyed Owls, an' LL.D. in Skowhegan Univarsity.

"An' all th' time th' wurruld was talkin' about this gr-reat binifacthor; all Mrs. Dochney cud find in her cold heart to say was, 'There's no fool like an' ol' fool' an' wint about her house wurruk an' made poultices f'r him whin he come fr'm th' meetin' iv th' Society f'r Pathronizin' th' Poor, where they'd give him a cold in th' chest fr'm th' Chautauqua salute.

"Well, sir, all times, good an' bad has got to come to an end, an' wan day Dochney come in to see me. 'I think,' says he, I'll go home an' go to bed and stay there. I've finished me will an' me life is no longer safe frim th' binificyaries. There's a prisidint iv a colledge comin' to town. He's an eager idjacator an' as I don't want to die with me boots on I think I won't see him. Here's that five cents I owe yer f'r th' sasprilly' he says. An' he wint away an' I niver set eyes on him again.

"He left a will iv five lines givin' all his money to

D—13

th' good woman an' sayin' that he thought he'd done enough f'r ivrybody else be keepin thim in hopes all these years, which is th' on'y pleasure in life.

"I niver cud undherstand a man like Dochney makin' money," said Mr. Hennessy.

"He made it," said Mr. Dooley, "because he honestly loved it with an innocent affection. He was thrue to it. The' reason ye have no money is because ye don't love it f'r itself alone. Money won't iver surrinder to such a flirt.

The Yacht Races

"In th' ol' times whin I was a yachtsman—" began Mr. Dooley.

"Scowman," said Mr. Hennessy.

"Yachtsman," said Mr. Dooley. "Whin I was a yachtsman, all a man needed to race was a flat-bottomed boat, an umbrella, an' a long dhrink. In thim days 't was 'Up with th' mainsail an' out with th' jib, an' Cap'n Jawn first to th' Lake View pumpin' station f'r th' see-gars.' Now 't is 'Ho, f'r a yacht race. Lave us go an' see our lawyers.' 'T is 'Haul away on th' writ iv ne exeat,' an 'Let go th' peak capias.' 'T is 'Pipe all hands to th' Supreme Coort.' 't is 'A life on th' boundin' docket an' a home on th' rolin' calendar.' Befure we die, Sir Lipton 'll come over here f'r that Cup again an' we'll bate him be gettin' out an over-night injunction. What's th' use iv buildin' a boat that's lible to tip an' spill us all into th' wet? Turn th' matther over to th' firm iv Wiggins, Schultz, O'Mally, Eckstein, Wopoppski,

Billotti, Gomez, Olson, an' McPherson, an' lave us have th' law on him.

"I don't suppose, Hinnissy, I ought to be gettin' off me little jokes on a seeryous matther like this. What's it all about, says ye? Well, ye see, 't is this way. Wanst befure th' war some la-ad fr'm this counthry took a boat acrost th' Atlantic an' run it again an English boat an' iv coorse, he won, not be-in' tied to th' dock, an' they give him a cup. He brought it back here an' handed it to a yacht club, which is an assocyation, Hinnissy, iv mimbers iv th' Bar. He says: 'Ye keep that cup on ye'er mantle-piece an' if e'er an Englishman wants it, don't ye give it to him.' Afther awhile, an Englishman that ownded a boat come afther th' cup, an' 't was lave go altogether, an' th' las' man to th' line knows what he is. He's an Englishman, iv coorse. That was all r-right too. But th' time come whin th' lagal pro-fission took a hand in th' game. 'Look here,' says they. 'Ye've vilated nearly all th' statues iv th' State iv Noo Jarsey already,' they says, 'an' if ye ain't careful, ye'll be hauled up f'r contimpt iv coort,' they says. So they took th' matther in hand an' dhrew up th' r-right pa-apers. 'State iv Noo York, county iv Cook, s.s. Know all men be these prisints. To all magisthrates an' polis officers, greetin'. In re Sir Lipton again th' cup. Ordhered that if Sir Lipton shall secure said Cup fr'm aforesaid (which he won't) he must build a boat as follows: Wan hun-dhered an' twinty chest, fifty-four waist, hip an' side pockets, carryin' three hundherd an' sixty-three thousan' cubic feet iv canvas; th' basement iv th' boat to be papered in green with yellow flowered dado, open plumbin', steam heat throughout, th' tin-ant to pay f'r all repairs. Be means iv this infernal machine, if onable to kill off th' rile fam'ly, he will attimpt to cross th' stormy Atlantic, an' if success-ful, will arrive at th' risidince iv th' party of th' first part, said John Doe. Wanst there, he will consult with mimbers iv th' Noo York Bar Association, who will lead him to a firm iv competent expert account-ants, who will give him his time, which is two min-yits mooourod bo th' invarse ratio iv th' distance fr'm th' binnacle to th' cook-stove, an' fr'm th' cook-stove, east be north to th' bowspirit. He will thin take his foolish boat down th' bay, an' if he keeps his health, he can rayturn to th' grocery business, f'r he's a jolly good fellow which nobody can deny.'

"Ye can see this, Hinnissy, that yachtin' has be-come wan iv th' larned pro-fissions. 'T is that that got th' la-ad fr'm Boston into it. They's a jolly Jack Tar f'r ye. In dhrawin' up a lease or framin' a bond, no more gallant sailor rides th' waves thin hearty Jack Larsen iv th' Amalgamated Copper Yacht Club. 'What ho?' says he. 'If we're goin' to have a race,' he says, 'shiver me timbers if I don't look up th' law,' he says. So he become a yachtsman. 'But, says th' Noo York la-ads, thim that has th' Cup on their mantlepiece, 'Ye can race on'y on two conditions.' 'What ar-re they?' says Larsen. 'Th' first is that ye become a mimber iv our club.' 'With pleasure,' says he. 'Ye can't,' says they. 'An' havin' complied with this first condition, ye must give us ye'er boat,' says they. 'We don't want it,' they says. 'Th' terms suit me entirely,' says Cap. Larsen. 'I'm a simple sailor man an' I'll give ye me boat undher th' following conditions,' he says. 'First, that ye won't take it; second, that ye'll paint me name on th' side iv it in red letters, three feet high; third, that ye'll inthrajooce me to th' Prince iv Wales; foorth, that I'll sail it mesilf. Nawthin',' he says, 'wud give me gr-reater pleasure thin to have me handsome an' expinsive raft in th' hands iv men who I wud considher it an honor to know,' he says. 'An' so,' he says, 'I'll on'y ask ye to sign a bond an' lave a small security, say about five hundherd thousan' dollars, in me hands in case anny paint shud be knocked off me boat,' he says. 'Yachtin' is a gintleman's spoort,' he says, 'an' in dalin' with gintlemen,' he says, 'ye can't be too careful,' he says.

"What's Sir Lipton doin' all this time?" asked Mr. Hennessy.

"He's preparin' his bond, makin' his will, an' goin' through th' other lagal preliminaries iv th' race. He's built a boat too. Th' King if England was aboord iv her, an' he was near killed, be havin' a mast fall on him. Th' Lord knows how he escaped. A mass iv steel weighin' a hundherd thousan' ton fell on his Majesty an' bounced off. Sir Lipton felt pretty bad about it. He didn't mind losin' a mast or two, but he didn't want annywan to know he had th' king aboord. 'T wud hurt business. 'Boys,' says he to th' rayporthers, 'th' King's on me yacht. Do

ye hear me? Th' King's on me yacht. But don't say
annything about it. I don't want to have it known.
Don't print it onless ye have to, an' thin put it in an
inconspicuous place, like th' first page. He's here
sure enough, boys. Th' mast just fell on his Majesty.
It nearly kilt him. I'm not sure it didn't kill him. He
remained perfectly cool throughout. So did I. I was
almost cold. So did both iv us. But, mind ye, not a
wurrud iv this in th' pa-apers.' I don't know how th'
rayporthers got hold iv it. But they're a pryin' lot."

"How did th' mast come to fall?" asked Mr. Hennessy, eagerly. "D'ye suppose Sir Lipton is wan iv
us?"

"S-sh," said Mr. Dooley, adding softly, "he was
bor-rn in Limerick."

On Golf

"Well, sir," said Mr. Dooley, "I don't want to say
annything that wud hurt a frind, but I do think th'
authorities ar-re very lax in lavin' Hogan at large,
as they ar-re doin'.'"

"An' what ails Hogan?" Mr. Hennessy asked.

"He's got what th' dock calls a fixed deelusion,"
said Mr. Dooley. "He thinks he's a goluf player. No,
he don't play th' game. Nobody does that. They
wurruk at it. But Hogan he slaves at it.

He don't think iv annything else. He takes it down
to th' wather-office with him in th' mornin', an'he
carries it home with him at night an' sleeps with it.
If ye go over to his house at this minyit ye'll find
him in th' front parlor swingin' a poker an' tellin'
th' good woman how he played th' eighth hole.

There's nawthin' more excitin' to th' mother iv siven
at th' end of a complete wash-day thin to listen to
an account iv a bum goluf game fr'm th' lips iv her
lifemate. 'Tis almost as absorbin' as th' invintory
iv a grocery store. I was over there th' other night,
an' he broke three panes iv glass showin' me what
he calls a mashie shot, an' he near took an ear off his
aunt Bridget practisin' with a war-club that he calls
a nibbelick. I wudden't be harsh with him, but a few
months or aven years in a well upholstered cell with
a ball an' chain on his leg, might restore him to himself an' make him again th' safe an' bashful husband
an' father he wanst was.

"But 'tis a gr-reat game, a gr-rand, jolly, hail-
fellow-well-met spoort. With th' exciption maybe
iv th' theery iv infant damnation, Scotland has given
nawthin' more cheerful to th' wurruld thin th' game
iv goluf. Whin 'twas first smuggled into this counthry, I cudden't make out what 'twas like. I thought
whin I first read about it that it was intinded f'r people with a hackin' cough, an' that no wan who was
robust enough to play 'Twinty Questions' in a
wheelchair, wud engage in it without a blush. I had
it in me mind that 'twas played iv a rainy afthernoon in th' front parlor. Th' two athletes got out
their needles an' their embroidery canvas, give a
shout iv glee an' flew at it. Th' results was submitted
to th' 'Ladies Home Journal,' an' me frind Eddie
Bok decided who was champeen, an' give him a goold
thimble f'r a prize.

"But I know betther now. 'Tis a rough an' angry

game, full of ondacint remarks an' other manly
charackteristics, d'ye mind. An' whin 'tis over it
laves as much bad blood as a German submarine.
At th' end iv ivry goluf match th' player loathes himsilf, is not on speakin' terms with th' fellow he
played agin, cud kill his own caddy an' his opponent's, an' hates th' criminal that laid out th' coorse,
th' game itsilf, th' Jook iv Argyll, each wan iv his
clubs, th' little bur-rd that twittered whin he was
shootin', th' pretty wild flowers on th' margin iv th'
links, an' each separate spear iv grass on th' puttin'-
green. If that Dutch poto that wroto th' 'Hymn iv
Hate' wants to write an-other on th' same subjeck
with a rale punch in it he ought to larn goluf. 'Twud
help him.

"How's it played, says ye? I don't exactly know.
I niver studied law. But ye can get th' rules iv th'
game in th' public library, in siven volumes edited
be th' Lord Chief Justice iv Scotland. If ye have a
dispute over th' rules, th' quickest way to get a decision is to hire a lawyer, make a test case, an' carry
it to th' supreem coort. In a gin'ral way, all I can
say about it is that it's a kind iv a game iv ball that
ye play with ye'er own worst inimy which is ye'ersilf, an' a man ye don't like goes around with ye an'
gloats over ye, an' a little boy follows ye to carry th'
clubs an' hide th' ball afther ye've hit it. Th' ball is
small, made iv injy rubber an' filled with a pizinous
substance, an' if ye hit it a good smash it busts an'
puts out ye'er eye. Ye're supposed to smash this
little grenade fr'm place to place an' here there an'

up an' down an' hither an' yon with an enormous insthrument iv wood or iron, ontill in due time ye get to what is called a puttin'-green. There's a little hole with a tin can in it in th' middle iv this place, an' whin ye're within a fut or two iv this hole ye take a small hammer out iv th' bag, an' ye hit th' ball four or five times till it tumbles into th' hole. Thin ye wipe th' cold sweat fr'm ye'er brow, write down '5' on a little card, an' walk away a few feet an' do it all over again.

"So far so good. But that ain't nearly all. Ye've got along pretty well, pokin' th' ball down th' pretty grass, whin wan day ye see a dark, evil-lookin' man watchin' ye. Ye mark him at wanst as ye'er inimy, an' well it is ye do, f'r he's th' expert that is layin' out th' coorse. He marks th' spot where ye'er best shot goes, an' says he, with a scowl 'I'll fix that crokey-playin' plumber.' An' he digs a hole five feet deep an' dumps a wagon iv soft coal ashes into it. Thin he picks out th' other places where ye loved to land, an' he puts in railroad ties, barbed wire, ditches, mounds, pizen-ivy, blackberry bushes, thrailin'-arbutus, a swamp, an' a field iv thistles, tears down a hill an' builds a mountain, gashes th' fair face iv nature with gapin' caverns an' chasms filled with gravel, cigaret stumps, brick-bats, sardine cans, hairpins, an' futprints, calls thim bunkers, an' goes his way. This pro-fissyonal torturer is what is known as a goluf archytect. If ye left a thurly good goluf archytect in th' garden iv Eden f'r an hour he'd make it look like Bilgium afther th' war.

"Well, ye play wanst through this jungle that a wire-haired tarryer cudden't get into, an' ye're told be a frind that ye ought to take a lesson. So ye pick out a bright-faced Scotch lad with a head shaped like a alligator pear an' who can hit th' ball a mile blindfolded an' ye give him what change ye have an' ask him to pint out ye'er faults. He pints out all ye'er wife has told ye about an' manny dark wans besides. I see Hogan takin' a goluf lesson wanst, an' how he iver dared to lift his head again is more thin I cud undherstand. Afther th' pro-fissyonal has recited th' catalog iv ye'er sins an' vices, an' ye've made an act iv conthrition, he tells ye how to hit th' ball. Ye'd think that ought to be aisy. Just go up an' give it a cuff.

"But it ain't annything like as soft as that. There ar-re forty different things ye have to think iv with each shot, an' if ye do wan iv thim wrong, ye're a lost soul. When ye'er idjication is completed ye go out an' do all th' things he told ye, but nineteen, an' th' ball skips lightly into a pit. Now is ye'er time to escape. If ye lave it lie there, turn ye'er back on it, run to th' parishhouse an' ask f'r th' prayers iv th' congregation, it may not be too late. Ye may be saved. Fly, weak an' wretched man, while ye have th' strenth! But if ye delay, if ye step but wan fut into th' thrap, ye're doomed an' on'y th' kindly hand iv death will release ye fr'm a life iv shame.

"Oh, 'tis th' jolly game, th' jolly ol' Scotch game. No wondher it's played all over th' counthry. Th' next pleasantest feelin' in th' wurruld to bein' perfectly happy is bein perfectly cross. That's why it's took up be middle-aged gintlemen. They want a chanst to go into a towerin' rage in th' open an' undher th' blue sky. To a goluf player, Hinnissy, th' spreadin' ellum three, a bloomin' rose bush, or a purlin' brook ar-re not what they seem to us. He don't use what ye call figures of speech about thim. No, sir, he uses a nibblelick or a fish-net.

"Another gr-reat injoocement to men to spind their Sundays on th' goluf-coorse is th' prisince iv th' fair sect. Hogan tells me there's nawthin' so pleasant to a tired player as to come up on a tee an' find in front iv him four beautiful ladies. Niver excipt in a sleepin'-car in th' mornin' ar-re ladies so atthractive as whin ye see thim fr'm a tee, with their lovely hair out iv curl, their tender faces tanned a lively pink or vermillion, an' a lumber jack's boots on their dainty feet, while they dab pitcheresquely at th' herbage or stand in graceful attichoods on th' puttin'-green correctin' each other's scoors. Their presence lights up th' whole landscape an' gives th' men players a chanst to rest an' gnash their teeth.

"Yes, sir, th' bravest an' th' best an' th' fairest can be seen, east or west, or north or south, beltin' away winter an' summer at this noble game or hallucynation or rite or whativer ye call it—sinitors, judges, congressmen, gr-reat iditors, preachers, th' prisidint himsilf. Whin a reporter wants to see Dock Wilson he don't look f'r him in th' White House. No, sir. But ye r-read: A riprisintative iv th' 'Daily Gloom' found th' Prisidint on th' eighteenth green. He seemed in very good spirits. Whin told that Count von Berstorff had set fire to th' threasury departmint, Ambassador Gerard had been pizened be th' Kaiser, an American battleship had been sunk be Cap Boy-Ed in th' North River, an' Dernburg was ladin' a charge iv th' turn-d'ye-mind armed with dumb-bells an' bowlin'-pins on Governor's Island, he laughed good naturedly an' said: 'We mustn't get too excited about this kind iv playfulness. I'll write thim a little letter th' first time we have a rainy day. By th' way, me boy, whin ye go down to ye'er office, I'd like ye to turn in this scoor an' tell th' spoortin' editor I missed a short putt f'r an eight at th' sixteenth. Otherwise I niver played betther.'

"Did I iver see th' game played? Faith, I did. Th' other mornin' I see Hogan go out with his kit iv tools. In other games wan bat is enough, but in goluf ye have to own twinty. All th' money that used to go f'r shoes in Hogan's fam'ly now goes f'r goluf-clubs. If he manages to hit th' ball with a club, he tells ye he wudden't part with that club f'r a hundherd dollars an' asts ye to feel it an' say ain't that a nice club. Whin he misses it he says th' club has gone back on him an' he buys a new wan. He has as manny implymints iv this new thrade iv his as a tinker. He has a hammer to beat th' ball into th' ground with, an' a pick to get it out, an' a little shovel to scrape it fr'm th' sand, an' a little hatchet to knock it into th' hole whin he gets near it. 'Where ar-re ye goin' with th' hardware?' says I. 'Is it to open a safe or build a battleship?' says I. 'I'm goin' to play goluf,' says he angrily. 'This is th' day I hang Larkin's hide on th' fence,' he says.

"So I followed him out to Douglas Park, an' there we met Larkin, who had a bag iv akel size. Hogan used to be champeen caber tosser iv th' ward an' Larkin was a sthructural ir'n-wurruker befure his health give out an' he become a horseshoer, but they groaned undher their burdens. Fortchnitly at that moment two bright little boys iv about eight years stepped up an' relieved thim iv their burden. 'What are these pigmies goin' to do with this here year's output iv th' Gary mills? says I. 'They're goin' to carry thim,' says Larkin. 'They're caddies,' he says. 'Well,' says I, 'tis very nice iv th' little toddlers. Th' young cannot start too arly in helpin' th' aged. But,' I says, 'why don't ye get up on their backs an' have thim carry ye around? A little more weight wudden't make much difference,' says I. 'Hush up,' says Hogan.

"Th' poor fellow was standin' on what they call th' tee, which is where ye take th' first lick at th' ball. He had a pole in his hand an' was swingin' it at a dandeline an' missin'. Ivinchooly he stepped up to where th' ball roosted on a little pile iv sand, stood with his legs apart like th' statue he calls th' Goloshes iv Rhodes, waggled th' stick in th' air, p'inted it tords th' pole, cried out, 'Stand away, Larkin, get round behind me, Martin, stop shufflin' there, boy,' an' screamed 'Fore' at a fat old gintleman that was at wurruk in a thrench three city blocks ahead. Thin he hauled off with th' bat, muttherin' to himsilf: 'Eye on th' ball, slow back, keep th' lift arm sthraight, pivot on th' right foot, folly through.' Up crept th' dhread insthrument slow an' cautious an' down it came with a blow that wud've foorced th' Dardanelles. I expicted to see th' ball splintered into a thousan' pieces or disappear into space. But it didn't. It left th' tee ridin' on a piece iv turf th' size iv ye'er hat, floated lazily off to wan side, dhropped, bounced twice, an' nestled in a bush. 'Watch it, boy,' yells Hogan. 'Watch it. Go right to it. Oh,' says he, 'what did I do that was wrong, what did I do?' says he, wringin' his hands. 'Ye dhropped Ye're right shouldher,' says Larkin. 'Took ye'er eye off it,' says Larkin's caddy. 'Toed it,' says an innocint by-stander. 'Ye made a mistake thryin' to hit at all. Ye shud've kicked it,' says I. Hogan stood by, his face convulsed with mortyfication ontil Larkin, a man whose Sunday mornin' recreation used to be raisin' a kag iv beer over his head fifty times, give a lunge at th' ball, done a complete spin an' missed it alto-gether. Thin a wan smile come to Hogan's lips. 'What ar-re ye haw-hawin' about?' says Larkin. They niver spoke again. Most iv th' time they weren't in speakin' distance iv each other. Fr'm time to time they wud meet be chanst on a puttin'-green an' Hogan wud say to himsilf: 'I'm down in twelve,' an' Larkin wud kick his ball over to th' next tee. So they wint rollickin' on. Hogan spoke to me wanst. He said: 'Dammit, stop coughin'.' Whin I left thim at th' sivinth hole th' excitemint was at its hite.

Larkin' was lookin' f'r his ball in a geeranyum bush, an' Hogan was choppin' down an evergreen three with wan iv his littel axes. 'Where ar're ye goin'?' says he. 'I don't know,' says I, 'but I may dhrop in at th' morgue an' listen to an inquest,' says I. 'I've got to spend me holiday someway,' says I.

"I see Hogan th' next day an' asked him why he played. 'Why,' says I, 'd'ye make a joke iv ye'ersilf at ye'er time iv life, an' ye a man with a family?' says I. 'That's just it, says he. 'I defy anny man in th' wurruld to get a bad lie in a bunker an' think iv anything else. He's that mad all his other sorrows, his debts, his sins, an' his future, disappears,' he says, 'like a summer cloud in a hur'cane. I'm that onhappy nawthin' bothers me. If a man come up an' told me me house was afire I'd not hear him. I don't know what it is,' says he, onless,' he says, 'it's th' feelin' that ye're bein' persecuted. It's ye'er since iv injustice that's stirred up in ye, that makes ye in-jye a round,' says he."

"Is th' Prisident a good goluf player, d'ye know, at all?" asked Mr. Hennessy after a moment of judicial silence.

"As a goluf player he cud give Lincoln a sthroke a hole," said Mr. Dooley.

MR. DOOLEY IMITATED

"A GOOD MANNY PEOPLE R-READ TH' OL' SAYIN' LARCENY IS TH' SINCEREST FORM IV FLATTERY'"

Note.—The following essay is an amalgam of a speech "delivered before the smoker of the second year class of the Harvard Law School, March 14, 1907 . . ." and an attempt by the compiler to add to it fifty-four more years of experience with the case system. For those who would like to see the original, it can be found at Harvard University both in Widener and at the Law School.

On the Case System

(with apologies to Mr. Dooley and "th' backers iv th' system.")

"I see be th' pa-apers," observed Mr. Dooley, "that all th' gr-reat institooshuns iv laygal l'arnin' in th' country have taken to th' case system."

"Niver heard iv a system that did me much good," muttered Mr. Hennessy.

" 'Tis that kind iv system, Hinnissy, but 'tis not likely it'll bother ye. 'Tis not backed be gamblers but be collidge perfessers and its victims aren't hod-carriers but those like Hogan, who must lose a few years becomin' lawyers before runnin' fer Congress. There are those Hinnissy, whose l'arnin' has gone to their tongues, who prefers callin' it th' cha-os method, but that's a bit too much fer ye.

" 'Twas someone with th' rich name iv Christopher Columbus Langsyne who started th' business. This here feller got lost in th' shelvin' in th' Harvid Lib'ry, an be th' time they discovered him, he'd gone an' read all th' cases from Doomsday to th' lates'

Supreem Coort dispatches. He was niver th' same
afther th' experience an' neither was th' law. 'Tis
said he read more cases than John L. drank, and
there are those who'll wager John L. could walk th'
sthraighter line.

"First thing ye know they made old Langsyne
Dean, an' he began advertisin' in th' Boston pa-apers
that a feller cud l'arn a bit iv law without studyin'
wan wor-rd iv lessons an' definitions th' same as in
school. This pa-aper said there was some gr-reat
lawyer-men there at Harvid, an' they knew so much
law all a feller had to do was to dally around
ferninst thim fer a year 'r two an' let it sink in—
ivry mornin' readin' what Holmes, J. or Cardozo, J.
or Marshall, J.—all Harvid men be th' way—have to
say about gas stokin', automobiles or fay-ries, about
which ye'd think they'd know nawthin'.

"It made hayroes iv these judges Hinnissy an'
twudden't surprise me some day if I heer some little kiddies swappin' five Frankfurters fer four
Blacks or two Potted Stuarts fer wan law clark—
'twud at laste be good fer th' bubble gum industhry.
Annyhow, to make th' system work, th' men who
wud profit most from it, printed a rosy raypoort iv
this most scandalous scheme an' it caught on like
chain letters. Twas like Congress votin' itself a
raise.

"In th' ol' days Hinnissy mention case to a lawyer an' he'd say Ol' Crow—at laste be th' beeogra-
phies—an' there are those who say th' law didn't
suffer be it although it was th' death iv manny a

D—14

good liver. Rough-house Choate didn't need Buster on Pleadin' to l'arn a jury how to be his. Dinny Webster—ah, I cud use th' man to pay me rent—an' Fallon an' Darrow were all case method men iv a kind Langsyne wud hold his nose up to, but 'tis not to say they weren't book-l'arn'd.

"There was manny story books on th' law thin, an' Kent did some writin' ontil he saw th' jig was up an' wint into th' cigarette business in th' nick iv time, an' there was an' old English wan called Cook on Littleton which I forbid Hogan to bring into me establishment. 'Twas a simple matter thin. In thim days all ye had to do was to sit at th' feet of an imminent lawyer—no mean feat, Hinnissy—read a little law as they say, and, if ye had th' looks, th' voice an' ye'er father in th' business ye was set fer lifers.

"Today, Hinnissy, ye go to law school fer three y'ars an' then ye have to ask th' sthreet car conductor where th' Coorthouse is. Ye'eve read all th' cases fr'm here to Chinee an' whin ye get into coort ye make ye'er first mistake be cross-examinin' th' bailiff an' ye'er secon' be commentin' on what a shtupid lookin' jury ye have to contind with as ye look at th' men in th' nice chairs behind ye. Ye think th' clerk iv coort sells dhry goods—if he did, he'd be sartin' to make th' briefs too long—an' ye think a charge to th' jury means which side can get to thim first. Hinnissy fer what most lawyers wind up doin' 'tis like tachin' a boy to run a cash raygister be sindin' him to that other timple of l'arnin' on th' wrong side iv th' Charles.

"Ye shud see th' kind iv problems they give th' boys before they let 'em loose on a suspectin' public. Hogan showed me his exam pa-aper wancet, an' niver again. Twas as sad an' sorry a story as I've ever read, like a woman's magazine, excipt it had no endin'. Th' poor hayroe was left bleedin', lost an' shellshock. 'Hogan,' I said, 'what's th' rest iv th' story. Me heart is sore fr'm cryin'.' Ye wudden't believe what Hogan told me. In th' story there was a little feller. Hogan, mercy be, called him an attractive nuisance. They had a saintly girl testifyin' to foul deeds. Hogan, impudent as iver, says not to believe a word she says because of a Hershey bar. An' ivry time I thought I was comin' to th' punch line Hogan wud puff his chest an' smile wisely an' say 'see Leach v Nutshell' or 'see Simpson v Stupidity' or some such nonsense. I'll see 'em, Hinnissy, but not in these familiar surroundin's.

"But to get back to l'arnin' be th' cha-os method—if ye please. 'Tis a game iv cards Hinnissy, an' th' house always wins. Each lawyer-to-be has to buy a stacked deck an' th' house always comes up with th' Jack-Ace to make a donkey out iv ye. An' whin ye think ye'eve got th' cards marked an' can give th' taycher a run fer ye'er money, don't ye think he knows it an' turns aroun' an' makes ye buy another deck. In th' ol' days a book iv law was good fer years on end but did ye iver here iv a case book outlivin' th' author. Not if his successor can help it. 'Tis a game an' like all games it has its followers includin' those that spend three years tryin' to bate it, a few who lave off in a week or so lackin' th' spoortin' blood as they do, an' wan or two brainy wans that laves off afther a year or two an' go into th' writin' business.

"An' thim that plays th' game'. —oh, 'tis a pitiful thing, Hinnissy, — 'tis awful. They git th' mos' turr'-ble gamblin' fayver. Whin thim boys ain't aytin' or slaypin'—which they seldom ar-re—they do nawth-in' but play solitaries with thim packs iv cases. They take wan case an' rade it over an' over, an' thin wancet again, an' they sip'rate ivry line fr'm th' wan nix' above an' below be gr-real black borders, so's not to git wan mixed up with t'other, an' they puzzle over ivry wor-rd, an' they bile it all down—or bile it away accordin' to th' run iv th' luck—an' thin they put th' bilin's into a schrap-book an' call thim 'ab-shtracts,' an' thin they bile thim abshtracts down, an' whin, afther they're all thru mixin' an' bilin', they go to tak' a fin'l invinth'ry iv what's in th' kit-tle, they foind it's full iv hot air.

"Be that as it may Hinnissy, 'tis a valuable experi-ence an' I have often thought that manny a horse-player belonged in law school for 'tis on th' thrack that abshtractin' an' underlinin' is no lost art—an' there are those who'll say vicey-versey.

"But ye have to see a case book to believe it. Ivry wan sued in these cases has a middle name beginnin' with a 'v'. Wan iv these days it'll be St. Vincent bat-tlin' Morgan Memorial. An' the names. Armry v. Delamire, Buick v McPherson, Eugene v Debs. Thin comes his honor—a feller always havin' a 'J' fer a

first name. I suppose 'tis as good a way iv pickin'
thim as electin' thim or havin' th' guv'ner pick' 'em,
that way it's called judicial selection, but me frind
Dochney, in th' eighth ward calls it courtship. Thin
th' case begins."

"Hinnissy wan day I'll read ye th' case about th'
constituchin follown' th' flag. Each case has a p'int
—if ye can find it—an' wan p'int builds on another
p'int an' sometimes a case takes away a p'int an' be
th' time Hogan came in fr'm class to do his study-
ing'—wan p'int leadin' to another—he'd soon be
edycatin' me patroons on th' finer p'ints iv th' law—
excipt in th' matter iv holdin' 'em.

"Now all that don' sound exactly enlightenin',
Hinnissy, but afther raydin' iv it over a couple iv
hundther' times with th' help iv a few dicsch'neries
an' grammers, an' givin' yer imaginash'n a bit iv
play, ye'd be surproised th' way th' pictoor gradoo-
ley onfolds befure yer eager eyes. Whin on th' next
day th' taycher sez, 'Mr. Hinnissy, shtat th' nix'
case,' here's what ye say: 'Whin A said, "Deed, I do,'
he sold Blackacre to B, and whin B promised to act
like a father to th' young immigrant girl on a promise to will th' land to her 'twas a misdeed.'

" 'Indeed,' says th' perfesser who gets a handsome
sum fer writin' introductions to books, and he then
adds p'ints to th' case an' takes 'em away ontil th'
lawyers-to-be agree that Blackacre is a stained glass
window an' that's what th' case meant. Some stu-
dents who read th' case ar-re given a boost, an' those
who haven't read it are made to feel they have on-

til it is suggested with as much cruelty as th' law will allow, that there is a shortage of French Legionnaires in Algeria. Th' treatment is such as th' case may require.

" 'Tis th' Suecratic method, Hinnissy. Suecrats was a Greek who cured ivrybody's problem but his own. Th' lawyers like him because he proved wancet fer all that if ye thry to be ye'er own lawyer ye have a ninny fer a client. He talked himsilf into th' lockstep an' th' hemlock, which is a drink, me frind, that me neighbor across th' sthreet makes ye pay to take.

"I don't undherstand," said Hennessy who was not easily confused.

"I'll give ye an example iv th' Suecratic method. Whin th' case is discussed to th' satisfaction iv th' taycher he says, 'Shtat th' nix' case.'

" 'Excuse me,' sez a student who has read all about Suecrats, 'but what does this case decide?'

" 'What shud ye say?' sez th' taycher.

" 'Oive not th' raymotes' idea,' sez th' student.

" 'Thin' sez th' taycher, 'Ye shtat th' nix' case.' "

On Contingent Fees

"Martin," said Mr. Hennessy, "What's all this hullabaloo about contin-gent's fees?"

"Ye been raydin' th' pa-apers agin, me frind. Ivry so often Hinnissy, a frind iv th' inshurence comp'-nies, usually their lawyer, makes a speech about— what did ye call it? Thin afther that th' Prisidint iv th' Naccas—which I'm told stands fer th' luck iv th' Irish—has a few kind words to say in difinse iv those

like himsilf who are th' Florince Nightingales iv th'
laygal world.   Despite th' confusion, Hinnissy, 'tis
really simple.   'Tis a simple fee.   In short, 'tis takin'
money fr'm th' simple.

"Suppos'n ye was to walk acrost th' sthreet afther
leavin' me place iv bizness.   'Tis dark an' ye'er more
worrid about wan leg makin' it afther th' other then
whether ye'll get there.   Along comes Schwartzmeister, thinkin' he's th' Kaiser, an' dhrivin his
German autymobile while readin' th' 'Gesundheit.'
He bumps ye an' if he had his glasses on an' cud
have seen who ye were he wudn't be sorry becus ye
buys ye refreshments here.   There ye ar-re a blot on
th' highway with nary th' strength to return th'
compliment. So what do ye do—ye get a lawyer, who
calls a doctor.

"Ye can't afford a lawyer, ye say. But ye get wan
jus' th' same.   Tain't justice, Hinnissy, 'tis democ-
racy. Ye tell Dorgan ye'er problem an' he says 'tis
worth a pretty penny, which is what ye'll get—Dorgan taken th' rest. Ye say to Dorgan, 'Tis a deal, me
lawyer-frind, if we win, ye take half, if we lose, ye
pay half to th' doctor.'   Twas all ye can do to keep
Dorgan fr'm boltin' out iv th' door, an' whin ye properly apologize, his partin' words ar-re, 'We win, ye
lose.' Th' reason inshurence comp'nies objict to this
ar-re manny, but inshurence lawyers don' like it fer
the're afraid th' principle iv th' contin-gent fee
might be practised on thim—on th' loosin's.

"An what does an inshurence comp'nee have to do
with ye an' Schwartzy. Th' truth is th' on'y purpose

ye and him sarve is to give th' case a name. Ye see th' jury knows Schwartzmeister is inshured or else he wuden't look so calm. Ye know all Schwartzy has in th' way of assits is four young 'uns, an a wife who eats fer two an' that Dorgan doesn't take his pounds in flesh. An' fin'lly ye know 'tis not Schwartzy's lawyer or else he'd be German. 'Tis what is called a laygal fiction, Hinnissy, which is th' on'y time Lady Justice admits to doin' a bit iv lyin'. An' th' proof—why to listen to Dorgan, ye'd think he got hit be th' dorry, an' to listen to th' inshurence man ye'd think th' money was goin' to be collleted fr'm th' jury. But whin th' case was all over ye an' Schwartzy had to be siparated in front iv th' restaurant across fr'm th' courthouse—while lookin' on eatin' together was th' lawyers. Th' rest iv what happens is above ye, but I'll tell ye annyway.

"Th' first thing ye know ye'er tol' ye wont live 'til trial, ye heart is finished, ye'er leg gimped fer life an' ye'll niver be able to put in a full days work, th' last iv it bein' thrue as such is ye'er inclination. Th' inshurence doctor examines ye an' says ye can do th' work iv three men, ye'er niver looked so fit an' recomminds bumpin' movin' finders as an exercise.

"Time passes, Hinnissy. Th' farst baby is born up on th' moon. Ye'er collictin' socyal security. Schwartzy's eldest is tendin' th' bar. Thin wan day ye ar-re tol' to appear in court in th' case iv Hinnissy vicious Schwartzmeister, S.S., wan party desarves another, an' manny happy presents to th' court officers. Ye'eve forgottin about th' case—ye an'

Schwartzy ar-re frinds agin but ye ar-re now th' sad victims iv indigestion in th' courts — which manes ye'er case is onsettled. Th' car is gone, ye have now a nat'ral limp, tho, an' ye have no throuble remembrin' what happened seein' that ye'eve forgottin all about it.

"Dorgan, greyin' at th' temples but still a gr-rand orator tells th' jury about ye'er aches an' pains ontil ye begin feelin 'em ye'ersilf. How th' sceeatica has run down ye'er head bone to ye'er spine an' into ye'er vericose veins. That ye'er aged horriby since its happend—an ye have—an' that ye'll niver again think iv goin' over Niagry in a barrel, a spoort ye didn't know enuf to take up th' on'y chance ye had. He says to th' jury, 'Money can niver repay me client fer th' damages that criminal did him but 'twill be all right with me. Will ye give him five cints an' hour fer th' pain an' th' work y'ars lost? Seein' me man comes fr'm a long livin' Irish clan an' at th' rate the're keepin' th' old alive these days he shud live to be 180. If me figure is correct ye'er verdict shud be fer $1,000,000.78 which is all I undherstan' th' Sioux Inshurence Comp'nee is worth.' Don't interrupt Hinnissy—I know Dorgan did a turrible thing mentionin' inshurence but it had nuthin to do with th' case, that is—Hinnissy—Hinnissy, ye'er thick an I'll not explain it.

"Thin Dorgan compliments th' jury on its intillegence, then finishes up with th' facts iv th' case as so: 'I might add, me bright eyed frinds that this is me first case iv exactly this kind while me frind here

has this type all th' toime, leavin' me at his mercy,'
an' he winks to th' bald-headed foreman. 'I might
also add me mother fr'm th ol' country—County
Co—Kerry,' he says to Flanagan, juror no. 2,' is de-
pindin' on me winnin' so she can have an operation
done.'

"Th' inshurence lawyer at this time objicts vi'-
lently an' wants to start all over agin an' accuses
Dorgan iv havin' a mistcarriage. If Dorgan was th'
man ye'd think him to be he'd a laid his frind cold,
but instead Dorgan rises an' says, 'An what has ye
agin me poor mother that washed floors to put me
thru collidge, ye heejus monsther.'

"Three jurymen had to be restrained fr'm attackin' th' inshurence lawyer an' once't th' judge, whin
he threatened Dorgan with contimpt iv coort fer de-
findin th' poor dear. Is there no shame, Hinnissy?
Dorgan fin'lly sits down a broken man. Ye l'arn later
that th' jury voted 14 to nawthin for Dorgan an' included th' courthouse in th' damages.

"Thin Schwartzy's man got up. A handsome well-
fed man that wud have made a good undhertaker.
First he asks th' coort to call off th' dogs an' forgit
about th' case an' he wont ask fer damages fer th'
dented fender. Then he looks over at ye, Hinnissy,
an' ye'd like to have crawled undher th' table. He
tells th' jury rollin' in th' sthreets was a common
past time to ye'er clan, an' ye got what was ye de-
serts. An' then he says even if ye didn't get ye'r de-
sert, 'twas th' best thing iver happened to ye—that
crutches was becomin' ye an' that in ye'er profission

a wooden leg wud earn ye more money in th' long run, that as fer th' bandages on ye'er face whin they took thim off it was a marked improvement an' even if ye didn't live so long 'twud be to others advantage if not y'ers. He then turned to Dorgan, picture iv sadness, 'Me brother here,' he says, 'says ye ar-re an intilligent bunch but I've heerd him afther manny a trial an' let me advise ye that his judgment is re-sarved. Me brother here seemed to be in awful pain but let me advise ye that th' man clappin' an' doin' handsprings whin me brother was thru is th' wan that ye'er payin' th' money to. Now ye gintlemen—an' excuse me—an charmin' lady—all work hard fer a livin', as I do mesilf. D'ye want to see this man walk out iv here an' loaf fer th' rest iv his life on th' earnin's kept fr'm widdies an' childhren because he didn't have sinse enuf to get his cigarettes in a store. I ask ye to see th' facts me way, me frinds'—an' he turned away to hide a tear—'fer befure I die I'd like to win wan case fr'm me brother Dorgan's mother.'

"Manetime th' judge was nudged be his hench-man, then whispered to, an' fin'lly shakin' so that while ye cudn't honestly say he was awake he was at th' laste talkin' be habit. 'Ladies an' gintlemen, if there be anny among ye,' he says, 'I mane ladies that is, me specs bein' left home, I cud spend half me life instructin' ye in th' rudiments iv th' law in this case but what fer. Ye've heard ivrything I have an' a bit more as is th' privilige iv wan iv me age, sta-tion, an acquaintances. I want ye all to go into th' jury room an' decide among ye what ye'll decide an' I'll give ye no assistance so th' vardict wont rest on me conscience.'

"As I said, ye wan th' case Hinnissy—'twas a good vardict, an' th' judge cut it in half, which ye didn't count on, thin Dorgan cut that in half, an' th' doctor took a good bit iv a nibble and be th' time it got to ye, 'twas like what wud remain iv a snowball if it rolled back up th' way it come down. So ye see Hinnissy, contin-gent fee 'tis not jus fer laygal sarvices; 'tis an' enthertainment tax, an' ye on'y have to pay if ye win.

"I wish't it happen'd," said Hennessy, dreaming, "'twas worth ivry bit iv it."

"That it was Hinnissy, and I'm sure if it was all so, that like Dorgan ye'd light a candle, as he's done fer manny a year, fer his sainted mother."

On Zoning

The following item appeared in the Concord (Massachusetts) Free Press for March 2, 1960.

Note.—Back in the early part of this century, that distinguished columnist Finley Peter Dunne began writing the famous Mr. Dooley series—Mr. Dooley being that redoubtable Irish gentleman: bartender by profession, social philosopher and commentator by inclination. Now we had supposed that Mr. Dunne alias Mr. Dooley was gone, but it would appear that he lives among us and on occasion is present at proceedings to which only his repertorial skill could do full justice. We feel doubly honored that he chose to attend such a recent hearing in our fair town, and to offer us the following observations which, co-incidentally of course, may sound reminiscent of his piece on "Immigration." [p. 82]

"Well, I see the Planning Board has got to wurruk again," said Mr. Dooley.

"Th' Lord save us fr'm harm," said Mr. Hennessy.

"Yessir," said Mr. Dooley, "they'se got to wurruk again, an' manny th' things that seems important to these bright young lads seems like-wise important to th' town residents—excipt for diff'rent reasons. Now divvle a bit do I care whither they use th' old asparagus farm f'r a cimitery or f'r housin'—with th' filter beds just acrosst th' way I'd as soon have th' breeze blow over th' livin' or th' dead, as over th' asparagus. An' let th' inshoorance comp'ny put up their buildin' even if it takes a bit of hoodwinkin'—what with a coort, a funeral home an' a cimitery in th' same block we c'n set up an assimbly line for th' dear departed, and keep stampin' 'em paid'til they reach th' Last Inspection.

"None but wan iv these questions int'rests me, Hinnissy, and be me I mane you an' be you I mane ivrybody. And as a pilgrim father that missed th' first boats, I must raise me claryon vice again' th' invasion iv this fair town be th' paupers an' arnychists iv effete Boston. Ye bet I must—because I'm here first!

"Twas diff'rent a few years back when we was the refuge iv th' college perfissor, th' archytict, ingineer an' raypacious lawyer. Now th' Plannin' Board says enuff's enuff—tho' as Shay sez about one iv 'em 'tother night, he sez, 'If th' Plannin' Board was five years ago what 'tis today, he'd be raisin' his voice iv protest in another town.' To which, be gorra, I add a pious 'Amen.'

"I keep tellin' Grogan, me only contact on th'

Board and me practic'ly born here, mine ye—I keep
tellin' him, 'An' wheere'll we get th' bright young
men to run th' town f'r us th' way we're plottin' to
keep 'em out . . . Like Willum Jennins Bryan our
prisent offishuls will be our bright young orators
'til they die, excipt f'r this—they'll be in office.'

"Don't always think ye're bein' persecuted, Hinnissy, for 'tis not a question iv restrictive covenants
—which Hogan tells me means 'Only England's sex-
tons need apply.' No sir, this Plannin' Board believes
in fair an' equal treatment for all—they don't want
anybody! Why th' way they're tryin' to take land
off the market it'd take 300 years to fill up a cimitery zoned for one acre lots!"

" 'Tis th' tax rate that worries 'em." said Mr. Hennessy looking up wisely from the Free Press.

"So 'tis, and it has me worrid half to death meself.
Seems only a French palace imported be Andhrew
Carnegie, with enuff land to hold a St. Pat's Day parade, can pay its own way. I hate to say it, Hinnissy,
knowin' yer modest means—but if it takes a $25,000
house to pay its own way, half iv th' residents iv
this town are charity cases an' 'tis ivry man to his
own poor house. An' who do ye think it is that's
keepin' out th' new? Why—'tis th' noovoo new,
that's who. I used to think 'twas th' poor that fought
th' rich's battles. I was wrong an' I know it—a man's
worst enemy is his own class!

" 'Tis th' chillun they're worrid about, is it? One
pint siven chillun to each new house? They're deci-
matin' th' poor little things to prove their pint! We

don't mind ye comin' in, sez they, but don't bring th'
chillun. Give us th' old an' unmarrid an' childless.
'Tis a modest little Plannin' Board proposal. A
Plannin' Board is no diff'rent than th' landlord who
says, 'No dogs, chillun an' easy on th' hot water.'

"Well," said Mr. Hennessy, "divvle th' bit I care,
on'y I'm here first, an' I ought to have th' right to
keep th' bus fr'm bein' over-crowded."

"Well," said Mr. Dooley, "as a pilgrim father on
me gran-nephew's side, I don't know but ye're right.
An' they'se wan sure way to keep thim out."

"What's that?" asked Mr. Hennessy.

"Teach thim all about our institooshuns befure
they come," said Mr. Dooley.

GLOSSARY, INDEX AND CASES